Kartheek Balapala

Neurophysiology of Extra Sensory Perception and Shamanism

GW00642883

Kartheek Balapala

Neurophysiology of Extra Sensory Perception and Shamanism

Pseudoscience includes beliefs, theories, or practices that have not been approved by scientific syndicates, but exist

LAP LAMBERT Academic Publishing

Imprint
Any brand names and product names mentioned in this book are subject to trademark, brand or patent protection and are trademarks or registered trademarks of their respective holders. The use of brand names, product names, common names, trade names, product descriptions etc. even without a particular marking in this work is in no way to be construed to mean that such names may be regarded as unrestricted in respect of trademark and brand protection legislation and could thus be used by anyone.

Cover image: www.ingimage.com

Publisher:
LAP LAMBERT Academic Publishing
is a trademark of
International Book Market Service Ltd., member of OmniScriptum Publishing Group
17 Meldrum Street, Beau Bassin 71504, Mauritius

Printed at: see last page
ISBN: 978-620-0-50579-8

Abstract

In early history, parapsychology was tangled up with astrology, numerology, magic and the occult, but is no longer associated with such forms of mysticism. Now only includes Precognition, Psychokinetics, Clairvoyance and Mental telepathy. There are now experimental techniques that conform to strict scientific methodology. History is full of examples of occult phenomenon which at sometime were caused by unknown factors. Their "mechanism" is being held up to standards that no science could pass and comprehend. The presence of Extra Sensory Perception (ESP) will not be considered as a science by most until the time comes when the scientists can describe what it is and the system that underlies it on paper. Only that current evidence does not seem to support it at this moment. It is pivotal to be highly critical of their existence until the mechanisms have been identified. If not sixth sense, then can any of the following like coincidence, failures to predict ignored, subconscious use of currently available information like sensory or via ESP or psychokinesis. Science: a process of inquiry, the process of formulating specific questions and then finding answers that give better understanding of mother nature. Pseudoscience does not use scientific method. In fact pseudoscience includes beliefs, theories, or practices that have not been approved by scientific syndicates, and no basis in scientific fact. This means disproved scientifically and can't be tested or lack evidence to support them. Yet this doesnot mean that they don't exist. Scientific explanations are based on the features of parsimony, generalization and tentativeness. Probably near death experiences (NDEs) might demonstrate the return of consciousness from death. Phenomenon of remote viewing supports the NDE and survival theory.

1

Contents

Introduction

Extrasensory Perception (ESP) – detecting information in some way other than through the normal processes of sensation.

Three Kinds of ESP:

- 1. **Telepathy** – mind-to-mind communication.

- 2. **Clairvoyance** – perceiving remote events. – Sense a friend hurt in a car accident

- 3. **Precognition** – perceiving future events. What would it be like if we could predict crimes?

- *. **Psychokinesis** – "mind over matter" such as levitating things.

All of these are considered paranormal phenomena. Parapsychology tries to study these scientifically. We can demonstrate using a simple coin flip demo.

How do people explain these strange experiences like clairvoyance?

Coincidence – events occur by chance.

Fallacy of positive instances – Our tendency to remember coincidental events that seem to confirm our belief about unusual phenomena and to forget all instances that do not (a type of confirmation bias)

Believers of ESP tend to be *less* accurate in their estimates of the probability of something happening by chance alone.

- For instance, what are the odds of having two people in a group of 30 having the same birthday? Actually, 7 in 10!

- OR Did you know that William Shakespeare was 46 years old when the King James version of the Bible was written. In Psalm 46 the forty-sixth word is "shake" and the forty-sixth word from the end is "spear."

- Was Kennedy the reincarnation of Lincoln?

If a person searches hard enough, they'll find these coincidences

Accuracy of psychics:

Make many predictions then the chance for a right one increases.

- "A person who talks a lot is sometimes right" – Spanish Proverb

- Analyses of psychic visions offered to police departments reveal that these are no more accurate than guess made by others (Reiser, 1982)

Vague predictions can later be interpreted to match events that provide a perceptual set for interpreting them.

After thousands of experiences, a *reproducible* ESP phenomenon has <u>never</u> been discovered, nor has anyone produced any individual who can convincingly demonstrate psychic ability.

Get the "The Million Dollar Challenge" by visiting James Randi's website homepage: www.randi.org

Ganzfeld Procedure:

Started by Daryl Bem and Charles Honorton – reduced the external distractions and had people try to perceive what someone in the next room was focusing on. (pg. 168-169 in Myers textbook).

Procedure places person in a reclining chair, with hissing white noise through headphones and shine diffuse red light through halved Ping-Pong Balls strapped over your eyes.

This is supposed to reduce distractions allow you to hear the thoughts from someone else inside your head.

The "sender" & "receiver" were placed in separate rooms with the sender concentrating for ½ hour on one of four randomly selected images.

Found 32 percent matched (chance would say 25%) but later studies did not reproduce this.

Can the Dreams Predict Future of people dreaming?

About 50% of university students think their dreams sometimes foretell the future (Messer & Griggs, 1989).

In 1937, Murray & Wheeler from Harvard tested this ability.

Example: After Charles Lindbergh's baby son was kidnapped and murdered but before the body was discovered, the researches invited the public to report their dreams about the child.

- Of the 1300 dream reports submitted, only 5% accurately envisioned the child dead.

- Only 4 of the 1300 correctly anticipated that the child was dead and buried among trees.

This number was no better than chance, but to those 4 dreamers the accuracy of their *apparent* precognitions must have felt completely real.

Ganzfeld experiments (ganzfeld is German for "whole field") have been around in some form since the 1930s. The studies that drew the most recent attention were done by Daryl Bem, a Cornell University psychologist, and Charles Honorton, a University of Edinburgh parapsychologist. Ganzfeld experiments involve covering a subject's eyes (generally with halves of ping-pong balls), bathing them in a red floodlight, and feeding white noise through headphones into their ears. This supposedly makes the subjects unable to receive sensory information. Then another person in a room shielded from the first subject tries to mentally send a specific picture. The first subject reports whatever imagery comes to mind and then tries to identify which of a group of pictures the second person was trying to send via ESP.

The idea here is that ESP is such a weak force, it is normally drowned out by our other senses. So with all other sensory input suppressed, the subject should be able to better use ESP.

Bem and Honorton used meta-analysis to combine the results of several studies, and found a hit rate of about 35%--enough above the expected chance rate of 25% to be significant, if true.

What makes people believe in ESP?

Correlation – Just because two events occur together doesn't mean they're connected or one causes the other. Correlation does NOT mean causation!

Confirmation Bias – People look for evidence that confirms their belief.

To note that………

Given the billions of events that occur each day and given enough days, some stunning coincidences are sure to occur

With enough time the improbable becomes inevitable

Extra sensory perception

Claims of **paranormal phenomena ("psi")** include:

Astrological predictions

Psychic healing

Communication with the dead

Out-of-body experiences

Extrasensory Perception (ESP)

Lack of Credibility of ESP

There is little to no **empirical evidence** of ESP

Perceived incidences of ESP:

Difficult to **replicate**

Might be a result of:

- **Intuitive judgment**
- **Chance**
- **Confirmation bias**

ESP and Law Enforcement

In a *survey* of **Police Departments** in **America's** *50* **largest cities**:

65% of Police Departments *never* used a psychic

Out of the **35%** who did, *none* found it substantially helpful

There are legitimate scientific tests for each type of proposed E.S.P. - Designed by real scientists at recognized universities

It may be interesting to note that both the United States (well, the CIA and DOD) and the Soviet Union researched E.S.P. heavily to try to gain an edge in the Cold War. For those interested, check it out on the Stargate Project.

In Paranormal-labs, researchers conduct a classic test to see if you are possibly either clairvoyant or precognitive

Most likely want to first look up information on tests created for each of these types

This lab may use Zener cards - named after the co-creator, Karl Zener who developed them at Duke University

Figure 1- Zenar cards

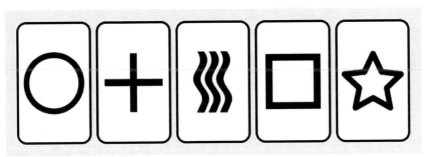

Zener cards

Did you see what I saw?

The idea (for clairvoyance) is, a researcher would hold up a card that the test subject cannot see

The test subject tries to see the hidden image with his/her mind

The researcher continues through the entire deck of 25 cards recording the number of correct and incorrect answers

The idea (for precognition) is, the test subject would tell the researcher what the next card will be.

The researcher then picks up a card and records the correctness

The researcher continues through the entire deck of 25 cards recording the number of correct and incorrect answers

If anybody wanna check and test it, then go to the following website:

http://www.psychicscience.org/esp3.aspx

(For clairvoyance) Select the Clairvoyance test, Open Deck, Cards Seen, and 25 cards

(For precognition) Select the Clairvoyance test, Open Deck, Cards Unseen, and 25 cards

Logical Possibility

The concept of logical possibility as distinct from physical possibility

Possible worlds as a way of talking about possibility

Necessity and contingency

What is logically possible: some hard cases – precognition and time travel

A final puzzle: are there really necessary truths?

Is ESP impossible?

All descriptions of ESP imply violations of conservation of energy...as well as violations of all principles of information theory and even of the principle of causality...Strict application of physical principles requires us to say that ESP is impossible---------Milton Rothman

Impossible? It depends on what you mean by impossible...

Does it actually happen?

Is it possible?

What do you mean by 'possible'?

Does ESP actually occur?

Is there any scientific evidence for or against ESP?

During the 1930s J. B. Rhine and colleagues at Duke University conducted a series of experiments to determine whether ESP phenomena actually occurred using Zener cards

What's wrong with Venckman's experiment (and with Rhine's original one)?

Face-to-face situation with minimal screening allows for 'sensory leakage'

In original, subjects could read figures from backs of cards

Subjects could see reflection in experimenter's glasses, or eyes

Subjects could read experimenter's expression, and voice

No double-blind

Rhine's results not duplicated when more rigorous experimental methods adopted

Logical Possibility vs. Physical ("Nomological") Possibility

Logically possible

'conceivable' and consistent: describing it doesn't imply a *contradiction*

Reductio ad absurdum is a mode of argumentation that seeks to establish a contention by deriving an absurdity from its denial, thus arguing that a thesis must be accepted because its rejection would be untenable.

Physically possible

consistent with "laws of nature"

Physical possibility, logical possibility and actuality

Whatever is actual is possible

…but not vice versa

Whatever is physically possible is logically possible

…but not vice versa

Possible Worlds: ways that things can be, could have been or could come to be

Actual world = possible world that we all live in

Researchers view possible world as a short hand convenient to discuss groups of possibilities

Accessibility: worlds we can can 'see'

A proposition (state of affairs), P, is possible at a world, w, if there's some world where P is true and w can 'see' that world.

12

We say a world that can be 'seen' from w is accessible to w

We understand different kinds of possibility in terms of different accessibility relations amongst worlds

Logical Possibility: All possible worlds are accessible.

Physical Possibility: Only those worlds at which the laws of nature are the same as they are at a given world are accessible from that world.

Possibility and necessity

Propositions are possible *at worlds*

- What's possible at a given world depends upon which worlds that world can 'see' (given the kind of possibility in question)

    - Logical possibility: assume we can 'see' *all* possible worlds.

For worlds, *w*, *w'*, where *w'* is accessible to *w* (*w* can *'see'* *w'*)

- *P* is *necessary* at world, *w*, iff at *all* accessible worlds, *w'*, *P* is true.

- *P* is *possible* at world, *w*, iff there is *some* accessible world, *w'*, at which *P* is true.

Intuitively, everything necessary is possible, but not vice versa.

We're interested in logical possibility so we don't have to worry about accessibility: P is logically possible iff there's some world at which P is true.

Some twisters about possibility

Transitivity of the accessibility relation

- Could Socrates have been an alligator? A bacterium? A virus? A Visa account with Bank of America? A number?

13

'Metaphysical' possibility: is there a kind of possibility 'between' logical possibility and physical possibility?

Twin Earth thought experiments:

- Is water *necessarily* H20?

- Can I conceive of a world at which *this stuff* fails to be H2O?

Salmon (1982) 'The Four Worlds Paradox'. To illustrate the puzzle: suppose that the actual world (w1) contains a bicycle, a, that is (actually) originally composed of A1 + B1 + C1, and suppose that there is a possible world, w5, containing a bicycle, b (not identical with a), that is originally composed (in w5) of A2 + B2 + C1 (where A1 ≠ A2 and B1 ≠ B2). Then, it seems, the application of the tolerance principle to each of a and b may generate two further possible worlds, in one of which (w6) there is a bicycle with the original composition A1 + B2 + C1 that is identical with a, and in the other of which (w7) there is a bicycle with the original composition A1 + B2 + C1 that is identical with b.

Summing Up

Logical possibility is possibility in the broadest sense.

A state of affairs is logically possible if

It is 'conceivable

Doesn't imply a contradiction

'possible world' is shorthand for 'way that things could be, could have been or could come to be'.

In possible worlds talk: a state of a affairs is logically possible if there is a possible world at which it obtains.

Necessity and Contingency

A proposition, P , *necessary* iff it has the same *truth value* at all possible worlds.

- *P* is *necessarily true* iff it is true at all possible worlds
- *P* is *necessarily false* iff it is false at all possible worlds

A proposition, P, is contingent if it has different *truth values* at different possible worlds.

- *P* is *contingently true*, iff P is true at the actual world but there is some possible world at which it is false.
- *P* is *contingently false* , iff P is false at the actual world but there is some possible world at which it is true.

Examples

Contingently true

The earth goes around the sun.

On earth, things fall at 32 feet per second per second.

The first day Fall 2015 classes at USD was Sep 2

San Diego is in California.

Contingently false

The sun goes around the earth.

There's no such thing as gravity--everything just floats.

The first day of Fall 2015 classes at USD was Sep 1

Lusaka is in Zambia.

Note: past tense sentences can be contingent even if we can't chance the past since the past could have been otherwise

To test whether a sentence is contingent, we try to tell a story about a possible world at which it has opposite truth value.

Sometimes this is straight-forward, but sometimes what seems to be such a story really isn't so we have to be careful!

"Lusaka is in Zambia" is one of those tricky cases.

Necessary or contingent?

How can we tell whether a true statement is *contingently* true rather than *necessarily* true?

Check to see whether you can *conceive* of a possible world at which it's false.

- If you can conceive of such a world, it's contingent

- If you can't it's either necessary…or you're lacking in imagination

But careful! Can we be absolutely certain about the character of our own mental states?

- *Can we mistakenly think we're conceiving of something when we're not—when we're conceiving of something different?*

Could Lusaka have been in South Africa?

"Lusaka is in Zambia" is **contingently** true if there's some possible world at which the city in which we now are isn't in Lusaka.

A proposition is contingently true if it's actually true and there's some possible world at which it's false.

But what seems to be a possible world that makes the proposition false may not really be one.

'Thought experiments' can be misleading!

Necessarily true

All bachelors are unmarried.

Que sera sera. [Whatever will be, will be.]

$2 + 2 = 4$

Either Lusaka is entirely in Zambia or Lusaka is not entirely in Zambia.

Necessarily false

Some bachelors are married

Some things that will happen will not happen

$2 + 2 = 5$

Lusaka is both entirely in and not entirely in Zambia

True in virtue of language

Be careful to distinguish between sentences which are true in virtue of language and those that are *about* language!

(1) is necessarily true but (2) is contingently true:

> (1) All bachelors are unmarried.
>
> (2) 'Bachelor' means 'unmarried male'.

Are mathematical truths necessary?

The course of maintaining that the truths of logic and mathematics are not necessary or certain was adopted by Mill. He maintained that these propositions were inductive generalizations based on an extremely large number of instances.

Even in a world of Ooblick, $2 + 2 = 4$. Even in a world without anyone who can do arithmetic $2 + 2 = 4$. Being non-physical doesn't mean being "merely subjective." "Mental" isn't the opposite of "physical" so to speak.

Precognition - Is it (logically) possible to 'see into the future'?

Time viewed timelessly: landscape *changes*

Four-dimensionalists contend that there is a deep analogy between the structure of ordinary material objects and the structure of the space-time of modern physics; three-dimensionalists question this analogy. Three-dimensionalists tend to embrace the slogan 'persisting things are wholly present at each time that they exist;' four-dimensionalists tend to reject it.

Precognition & the Open Future - The secular version of the problem of God's foreknowledge

Precognition & Psychic Predictions:

If the psychic was right, then it was true at t1 that e was going to happen at t3

But you immediately take action a in order to prevent e from happening

You're successful! At t2 it isn't true that e was going to happen at t3

Is this logically possible???

Tensed vs. timeless propositions

Let us assume that at on September 6 the psychic 'looked into the future' and saw e occurring at September 8.

On Saturday, September 6, she says, 'In the future, two days from now, e will occur'.

What she said can be translated into the *timeless* sentence:
e **occurs** on monday, September 8, 2014.

Timeless propositions

18

If the psychic was correct, then the following timeless sentence was true on Tuesday: Event e OCCURS on Tuesday, September 9, 2014.

But following her advice, you immediately do an action, a, that prevents e's occurring.

So whereas it was true on Sat, Sept 6 that e would OCCUR on Mon, Sep 8 (the psychic 'saw' it coming) it was no longer true at Sunday.

But wait! If the Psychic was right on Tuesday that e was going to occur in two days then it is *timelessly true* that e **OCCURS** on Thursday

And if timelessly true, it was true at all times…including Saturday!

So it looks like we have a contradiction: *timelessly* both

- *e occurs* on Monday (because the psychic was correct) and

- *e does not occur* on Monday (because a prevented it)

Logic deals with logical possibility

The possibility of propositions being true (necessity and contingency)

The possibility of groups of propositions all being true together (consistency)

The impossibility of the premises of an argument being true and the conclusion being false (validity)

A puzzle: is necessity possible?

How can there be necessary truths? Take "all bachelors are unmarried": I can describe a world were "bachelor" means "male under 30" and such a world is one in which there are married bachelors, right? Similarly "2+2=4" and "2+2=5": it's just a matter of how you define the symbols, right?

Skeptic:

Embodies in the scientific method

Skepticism is a METHOD leading to conclusions

A skeptic is one who questions the validity of a particular claim by calling for evidence to prove or disprove it

"That's nice…prove it"

Universal Skepticism:

The reality of the senses and the validity of rational inference should be mistrusted.

Philosophy: this has led to Extreme Solopsism: The reality of the external world and even one's existence are doubted. Universal Skepticism is negative, self-defeating, and contradictory.

Selective Skepticism: If a finding seems scientifically valid, it is accepted, until a better theory comes along to replace it. There are NO absolute laws !

Science

A set of methods designed to describe and interpret observed or inferred phenomena, past or present, and aimed at building a testable body of knowledge open to rejection or confirmation.

Scientific Principles are:

Induction - Forming a hypothesis from existing data

Deduction - Making specific predictions based on hypothesis

Observation - Gathering data, driven by our hypothesis that tells us what to look for

Verification - Testing the predictions against further observations to confirm or falsify the initial hypothesis.

Via the scientific method we can come to the following conclusions:

Hypothesis - A testable statement accounting for a set of observations

Theory - A well-supported and well-tested hypothesis = evolution

Fact - A conclusion confirmed to such an extent that it would be reasonable to offer provisional agreement = The earth is not flat

Rationalism - Basing conclusion on logic and evidence

Dogmatism:

Basing conclusion on authority

Parents said so, I said so, Textbook says so

Science = How to ALWAYS think about explaining the universe…

Systematic Empiricism = relying on observation

Production of Public Knowledge = Findings must be presented to the community in such a way that they can be replicated, criticized or extended by anyone

Examination of Solvable Problems = Predict, then Control and Explain

Mystery back then…Problem now!

Falsifiability:

Scientific theories must be presented in a way so as that they can be shown to be false.

What "SHOULD" happen and what will "NOT" happen

Predictions on Peter: He SHOULD develop some sort of behavior related to the loss of his parent, how it manifests itself is TBD.

Peter will NOT develop the power to kill a tiger from 40 yards with mind bullets, on account of his parents demise.

Extraordinary claims need extraordinary proof!

Science is open minded: Believers are NOT!

Parapsychology

Parapsychology - the field of study concerned with the supernatural or other phenomena that science cannot explain.

AKA – Phony, fake, or unscientific psychology.

Dangers of Para/Pseudopsychology:

Can cause: Beliefs of racial superiority, Beliefs of demonic possession as a cause of metal illness, Lobotomies Etc

Confirmation Bias – We pay attention to events that confirm our beliefs and ignore evidence that contradicts them.

Fraud – Waste time, money, and talent on inaccurate methods.

Can be used to falsely confirm racial or sexual stereotypes.

Acceptance of inaccurate methods for treating psychological disorders- Facilitated communication

Psychology – The scientific study of behavior and mental processes.

Behavior – An action that other people can observe or measure.

Goals of Psychology:

Explain, predict, and control behavior.

Psychologists organize their ideas about behavior and mental processes into theories.

Theory – A statement that attempts to explain why things are the way they are and happen the way they do.

Parapsychology is the study of unexplained mental phenomena.

Studied in over 30 countries (United Kingdom)

Funded by donations

Society of Physical Research (1882)

OBE- Feeling of departing from one's physical body.

Reincarnation- To return after death in a newborn body.

Poltergeist- troublesome spirit that mischievously moves domestic items.

Haunting- Past peopleor things that are now dead but continue to cause disturbances.

Skeptics

Biased Evidence - parapsychology needs to breakdown the division between "skeptic" and "researcher."

Fraud - Deceit or trickery, intended to gain some unfair or dishonest advantage.

Media – deals with

UFOs

vampires

alchemy (King Midas)

witchcraft

searching for Bigfoot

Reasons to Continue Study

It IS a Science

Beneficial to other Sciences (Astrology)

Useful in other psychologies

The other kind:

Alien Abductions

Hyponosis

Psychiatric hospitals

Most sciences try to explain observable phenomena. Parapsychologists try to observe unexplainable phenomena.

Telepathy

A *telepath* would be a person with the paranormal ability to read others' thoughts and mental contents.

It may involve one person sending thoughts to another or perceiving another's thoughts without using any of the five recognized senses.

Term was coined by F. W. Myers in 1882.

Popularized by fictional novels and movies.

Clairvoyance

French for "clear seeing"

The ability to "see" information about people, objects, or locations without using any of the five senses.

Includes crystal gazing and tea leaf reading.

Precognition

Dream interpretation

Many people believe dreams   predict the future

Ex. Joseph in the Old   Testament

Example:

I had a recurring dream every night for a month. In the   dream my father, who was dead in reality, paid a visit   and told me. 'You will not see Doug and Joy again. They will not be here long'. Doug and Joy were my brother and his wife.

The dream was very disquieting and I wanted to warn my brother but my husband told me not to be so 'silly'. Two days after the last dream I bought the local paper and on the front page were my brother and Joy. They had been killed flying to Senegal. I had no idea they had gone on   holiday.'

What the Skeptics Say

After thousands of experiments, a reproducible ESP phenomenon has never been discovered, or has anyone produced any individual who can convincingly demonstrate psychic ability.

A National Research Council investigation of ESP concluded that "the   best available evidence does not support the contention that these   phenomena exist."

The best scientific evidence does not justify that ESP -that is, gathering   information about objects or thoughts without the intervention of known   sensory mechanisms- exists.

If science can't fully explain the phenomena COMPLETELY, reasonable explanations are ignored or dismissed and the proponent concludes that pseudoscience is supported. This can be dangerous

Gothic supernatural

Gothic literary works are dedicated to horror stories, the fantastic, and the "darker" supernatural forces. The English Gothic novel took origin with the publication of Horace Walpole's The Castle of Otranto (1764), which Walpole called a "Gothic story." Three of the novels for this class includes Frankenstein, Wuthering Heights, and Dracula, belong specifically to the Gothic genre, but Gothic or supernatural motifs are important in all the works we'll read.

Though the Gothic period began to fade at the birth of the modern science and "Age of Reason," after lasting for approximately 70 years [the last published work of the explicitly Gothic genre appeared in 1834 – Charles Maturin's Melmoth the Wanderer], that influenced most of the emerging genres. The unique portrayal of the alluring antagonist with evil characteristics can be obvious that appeal to our sense of awe, the melodramatic aspects of romance, or the motif of a persecuted maiden forced apart from a true love.

Gothic literature got name from its similarities to the Gothic medieval cathedrals, which feature a majestic, unrestrained architectural style with often savage or grotesque ornamentation. Word "Gothic" came from "Goth," the name of one of the barbaric Germanic tribes that invaded the Roman Empire way back in history.

Gothic Architecture:

Majestic, unrestrained architectural style

Profusion of savage, often grotesque ornamentation

The vaulting arches and spires of Gothic cathedrals reach wildly to the sky as if the builders were trying to grasp the heavens. The cathedrals are full with a profusion of wild carvings depicting humanity in conflict with supernatural forces—demons, angels, gargoyles, and monsters.

A motif means repeated theme, image, or literary device.

Like Gothic architecture, Gothic literature focuses on humanity's fascination with the grotesque, the unknown, and the frightening, inexplicable aspects of the universe and soul of humans. The Gothic relates the individual to the infinite universe and demonstrates horror by portraying human individuals in confrontation with the overwhelming, mysterious, horrendous forces found in the cosmos and within themselves. Gothic literature depicts the human status as an ambiguous mixture of good and evil powers that cannot be understood completely by human reason. Thus, the Gothic perspective conceives of the human situation as a paradox, a dilemma of duality—humans are divided in the conflict between opposing forces in the world and in themselves. The Gothic themes of human nature's depravity and duality with the struggle between good and evil in the human soul, and the existence of unexplainable elements in humanity and the cosmos, are prominent themes. These common supernatural/Gothic motifs are quite obvious.

The Doppelganger:

A second self or alternate identity

Represents opposing forces in human nature

Suggests humans have a double nature

Forbidden Knowledge or Power/ Faust Motif:

Forbidden knowledge/power is frequently the Gothic protagonist's goal. The Gothic "hero" questions the universe's ambiguous nature and comprehends to control those supernatural powers that mortals cannot understand. He tries to overcome human limitations and turn into a "god." This ambition leads to the hero's downfall and destruction. But, Gothic tales of ambition sometimes paradoxically evoke our admiration because they patronize individuals with the courage to defy fate and cosmic forces in an attempt to transcend the mundane to the eternal and sublime.

Monster/ Satanic Hero/ Fallen Man:

Fallen Hero becomes a Monster

Or, confronts a monster who is his double

Like Satan, he defies the rules of God's universe

Demons/ Devils/ Witches/ Angels:

Represent conflicting forces in the human soul

Hero may be tempted by evil spirits

Or, redeemed by good spirits

Magic Talismans:

Symbolize supernatural forces

Or, forces in the hero's personality

Dreams / Visions: Reveal hidden truths of the unconscious mind

Signs / Omens: Reveal intention of cosmic forces. Often represent psychological or spiritual conflict.

Graveyards / Churches / Ruins: Suggest human confrontation with infinite forces

Haunted Castle or House: Reflects Hero's Psychological character

Multiple Narrative:

Series of secret manuscripts or multiple tales

Narrative spirals inward to hidden truth

Narrator compelled to speak to captive listener

Madness: Reflects realities beyond rational comprehension, Mad characters speak truths we wish to deny.

Blood: Symbolizes paradox of human condition. Represents life/death, guilt/innocence

Other Motifs:

Murder

Incest and sexual perversion

Value reversals

Mistaken/secret identities

Dichotomies

Innocence victimized by evil

Circuits in human brain

The **central nervous system [CNS]** is composed entirely of two kinds of specialized cells: *neurons* and *glia*.

The human brain has approximately 100 billion neurons. To learn how neurons carry messages, read about the action potential.

Glia (or **glial cells**) are the cells that provide support to the neurons

Communication between neurons, or nerve cells, is the cellular basis for thinking

Synapse- A place where nerve signals are sent across a gap.

A synapse is a small gap at the end of a neuron that allows information to pass from one neuron to the next. Synapses are found where nerve cells connects with other nerve cells as well as where nerve cells connect with muscles and glands

Synaptic cleft = 0.02 micron

Cerebral cortex

Executive functioning capability = thinks

Gray matter: of neuron cell bodies, dendrites, short unmyelinated axons

100 billion neurons with average of 10,000 contacts each

Has No fiber tracts (other wise would be white)

2-4 mm thick

Brodmann areas (historical: 52 structurally different areas given #s)

Neuroimaging: functional organization

Prenatal life: <u>genes are responsible</u> for creating the architecture of the brain

<u>Cortex is the last to develop</u> and very <u>immature at birth</u>

Birth: excess of neurons <u>but not inter-connected</u>

1st <u>month of life</u>: a million synapses/sec are made; this is genetic

1st <u>3 years of life</u>: synaptic overgrowth (<u>connections develop</u>)

After this the <u>density remains constant</u> though some grow, <u>some die</u>

<u>Preadolescence</u>: another <u>increase</u> in <u>synaptic formation</u>

Adolescence until 25: brain becomes a <u>reconstruction site</u>

Connections important for <u>self-regulation (in prefrontal cortex</u>) are <u>being remodeled:</u> important for a sense of wholeness

If personal turbulence, <u>Susceptible to stress</u> and toxins (like alcohol and drugs) during these years; affects the rest of one's <u>life style and philosophy</u>

The <u>mind changes the brain connections</u> (=malleability = throughout life, according to stimulation, local culture and circumstances)

Where brain <u>activation occurs, synapses happen</u>

When <u>pay attention & focus mind</u>, neural firing occurs and brain structure changes (<u>synapses are formed</u>)

Human connections have impact on neural connections (<u>ongoing experiences and learning</u> include the interpersonal ones)

How to focus our mind ?

Mind Vs Brain. Any difference ?

Malleability – eg: singer, guitarist, legal judge, cinema director, surgeon, psychiatrist….

All the neurons are *interneurons*

By definition confined to the CNS

They have to synapse somewhere before the info passes to the peripheral nerves

Three kinds of functional areas in cortex

Motor areas: movement

Sensory areas: perception

Association areas: integrate diverse information to enable purposeful action

Sensory areas -*Posterior to central sulcus*

Primary somatosensory cortex: postcentral gyrus of parietal lobe (allows conscious awareness of sensation and the ability to localize it: *where* the sensation is from)

Somatosensory association area: behind it   (understanding of what is being felt: the *meaning* of it)

Sight: occipital lobe

Primary visual cortex (17)

Handles info from contralateral retina (right ½ of visual field is on left side cortex)

Map of visual space

Face image felt

If damaged: functionally blind because no conscious awareness of sight

Visual association area (18 & 19)

Face recognition is usually on the right side

Hearing: temporal lobe

Primary auditory area (41)

Auditory association area (22)

Smell (olfactory sense): uncus -Deep in temporal lobe along medial surface

Motor areas -*Anterior to central sulcus*

Primary motor area

Precentral gyrus of frontal lobe (4)

Conscious or voluntary movement of skeletal muscles

Precentral gyrus of frontal lobe

Precise, conscious or voluntary movement of skeletal muscles

Large neurons called ***pyramidal cells***

Their axons: form massive ***pyramidal* or *corticospinal tracts***

Descend through brain stem and spinal cord

Cross to contralateral (the other) side in brainstem

Therefore: ***right side of the brain controls the left side of the body, and the left side of the brain controls the right side of the body***

Broca's area (44): specialized motor speech area

Base of precentral gyrus just above lateral sulcus in only one hemisphere, usually left

Word articulation: the movements necessary to produce speech

Damage: can understand but can't speak/lecture; or if can still speak, words are right but difficult to understand for others

Premotor cortex (6): complex movements asociated with highly processed sensory info; also planning of movements

Frontal eye fields (inferior 8): voluntary movements of eyes

Body map: entire human body spatially represented – (like concept map)

Where? on cortex; upside down – both sides – Homunculus

Association **areas: everything else**

Tie (link) together different kinds of sensory input

Associate new input with previous stored memories = so learning= new memory = redefine emotions = change in attitude & behaviour = Higher education

Our brain is programmed to be passive (by elders) since birth. Reprogram yourself through genuine education and training

Is to be renamed *"higher-order processing" areas*

Prefrontal cortex: cognition

Intellect

Abstract ideas

Judgment

Personality

Impulse control

Persistence

Complex

Reasoning

Long-term planning

Social skills

Appreciating humor

Conscience

Mood

Mental flexibility

Empathy

Logic

Executive functioning

e.g. multiple step problem solving requiring temporary storage of info (working memory)

Then how can we make up ideas ?

Ideas come from the interaction of default network (Primary areas) with the executive network (Association cortex) of circuits in cortex.

Wernicke's area

Junction of parietal and temporal lobes

One hemisphere only, usually left

(Outlined by dashes)

Pathology: <u>comprehension</u> <u>impaired</u> for written and spoken language: output fluent and voluminous but not coherent- <u>Vit B1 deficiency, alcohol abuse</u> (opposite with Broca's area). General confusion state, disinterest, inattentiveness.

Right brain Vs Left brain

left brain is <u>conscious mind</u>, and right brain is <u>subconscious mind</u>.

<u>Ancient People</u> are right-brain dominated people : Einstein, Leonardo Da vinci (creative)

<u>Modern People</u> are left-brain dominated people : local leaders (calculated)

<u>Ideal People</u> are balanced (midbrain) dominated -When both left and right brain are in balance use, we become more resourceful and have great love to offer- no wars will happen (blind fold reading method, typing tutor)

Idealists = create a new culture, modifying current beliefs

Ideal society= every body wins equally, but in a different dimension

(everybody = both good people and not good people)

Philosophy = mindset/belief in life

Vision = future goal

Mission = goal at present moment

Magic uses pure logic of making things happen, but no powers

Homunculus – Entire body in the brain

A homunculus is used to describe the relative amount of space our body parts occupy in the brain.

In a model of motor functions, some parts are much bigger because we use them much more, or with more accuracy.

The more we use a part of our body, the more space our brain needs to control or interpret it.

In fact, by learning the brain may have to change the space it uses to account for new abilities.

Evidence from neuroscience

People who play music have been found to have auditory centres that are BIGGER than normal.

The 'sound' area of their brain grew through practising their music.

Rats in a rich environment have heavier brains, by 10%, than those in a boring environment. Taxi drivers have bigger areas which deal with 3D space – the hippocampus - than non-taxi drivers.

Musicians have a larger auditory cortex.

All of the areas of the brain …like sound, communication, problem-solving…are made of cells called **NEURONS.**

They transmit information all around the brain.

Neurons pass information through CONNECTIONS with other neurons at SYNAPSES

Learning helps our neurons GROW.

The more we learn, the more connections they make.

People with large auditory areas in their brain grew lots more neuron connections in the sound area through lots and lots of practice.

Chemical Synapses

Components

Presynaptic terminal

Synaptic cleft

Postsynaptic membrane

Neurotransmitters released by action potentials in presynaptic terminal from synaptic vesicles

Diffusion into

Postsynaptic membrane

Neurotransmitter removal occurs after the activity is done

Flow is unidirectional

Electrical synapse

At electrical synapses, gap junction channels allow a direct communication between the cytoplasm of the two coupled cells. In addition to ions (black circle), and metabolites (blue), small second messenger molecules (orange) can also diffuse through gap junction channels.

Electrical transmission via the intercellular channels can be bi-directional

Neurones & the Action Potential

Neurones conduct impulses from one part of the body to another.

Myelinated Axons - The axon is a single long, thin extension that sends impulses to another neuron. They vary in length and are surrounded by a many-layered lipid and protein covering called the myelin sheath, produced by the schwann cells.

Impulses travel very rapidly along neurons. The presence of a myelin sheath greatly increases the velocity at which impulses are conducted along the axon of a neuron. In unmyelinated fibres, the entire axon membrane is exposed and impulse conduction is slower.

Three types of nerves

Afferent nerves are composed of sensory nerve fibers (axons) grouped together to carry impulses from receptors to the central nervous system.

Efferent nerves are composed of motor nerve fibers carrying impulses from the central nervous system to effector organs, such as muscles or glands.

Mixed nerves are composed of both afferent and efferent nerve fibers.

Classification of nerve fibers

The first system, described by Erlanger and Gasser, applies to both sensory (afferent) and motor (efferent) nerve fibers and uses a lettered nomenclature of A, B, and C.

The second system, described by Lloyd and Hunt, applies only to sensory nerve fibers and uses a Roman numeral nomenclature of I, II, III, and IV.

ERLANGER - GASSER CLASSIFICATION

Fiber type	Diameter(m)	Conduction velocity(m/s)	Function
A			
α	12-20	70-120	Proprioception: somatic motor
β	5-12	30-70	Touch, pressure
γ	3-6	15-30	Motor to muscle spindles
δ	2-5	12-30	Pain, cold, touch
B	<3	3-15	Preganglionic autonomic
C			
Dorsal Root	0.4-1.2	0.5-2	Pain, temperature
Sympathetic	0.3-1.3	0.7-2.3	Postganglionic sympathetic

A and B fibers are myelinated

C fibers are unmyelinated.

NUMERICAL CLASSIFICATION FOR SENSORY NEURONS

Number	Origin	Fiber type
Ia	Muscle spindle, annulospiral ending	Aα
Ib	Golgi tendon organ	Aα
II	Muscle spindle, flower spray endings; touch, pressure	Aβ
III	Pain and cold receptors	Aδ
IV	Pain , temperature	Dorsal root C

Number IV---- not myelinated

Demyelinating Diseases: Affect somatic, visceral afferents, motor

Pain and temperature not affected

Sensations felt by humans

Comparison of General and Special Senses

<u>General sensations are</u>

Include somatic sensations (tactile, thermal, pain, and proprioceptive) and visceral sensations.

Scattered throughout the body.

Simple structures.

<u>Special senses include</u>

Include smell, taste, vision, hearing and equilibrium.

Concentrated in specific locations in the head.

Anatomically distinct structures.

Complex neural pathway.

Olfaction: Sense of Smell

Olfactory epithelium contains 10-100 million receptors inside the roof of nasal cavity.

Olfactory receptor- a bipolar neuron with cilia called olfactory hairs - Respond to chemical stimulation of an odorant molecule.

Supporting cells- provide support and nourishment.

Basal cells- replace olfactory receptors.

<u>Neurophysiology of Olfaction</u>

Humans can detect about 10,000 different odors.

Odorant binds to the receptor of an olfactory hair→ G-protein activation→ activation of adenylate cyclase→ production of cAMP→ opening of Na+ channels→ inflow of Na+ →generator potential→ nerve impulse through olfactory nerves→ olfactory bulbs→ olfactory tract→ primary olfactory area of the cerebral cortex.

Anosmia -absence of the sense of smell

Hyposmia-diminished olfactory sensitivity

Dysosmia -distorted sense of smell

Pheromones:

Effects sexual behavior, territorial behavior and identification of kin- infants - correctly identify their own mother's milk and are much more likely to nurse when its their own mom

Female menstrual cycles - altered - pheromones - the sorority effect

Affect male and female behavior- (*alpha androstenol)*- human pheromone

Sensation of taste

Taste bud- made of three types of epithelial cells: supporting cells, gustatory receptor cells and basal cells. About 50 gustatory cells per taste bud. Each one has a gustatory hair that projects through the taste pore. Taste buds are found in the papillae.

Three types of papillae: vallate (circumvallate), fungiform and foliate.

Five types of taste: sour, sweet, bitter, salty and

Tastant dissolves in saliva → plasma membrane of gustatory hair→ receptor potential→ nerve impulse via cranial nerves VII, IX and X→ medulla→ thalamus(VPN)→ primary gustatory area(43) of the cerebral cortex.

Taste Blindness -15 to 30 per cent of all people exhibit taste blindness- to thiourea compounds

SALT TASTE:

Receptor ----- enac

Blocker------ amiloride

Neurotransmitter released ----- glutamate

SOUR TASTE:

H+ is responsible

Hcn – hyperpolarization activated cyclic

Neucleotide- gated channels

UMAMI TASTE:

Receptors --- mglur 4

Agonists--- Purine 5 – ribonucleotides i.e., IMP , GMP

Taste Eg;

Breast milk

Ripe tomatoes

Fish

Mushrooms

Fermented fish sauce

BITTER TASTE:

24 different receptors of t2r family

linked to gustducin(g protein)

SWEET TASTE:

Receptor is coupled to a G-protein that activates protein kinase A and causes it to phosphorylate and block a potassium-selective channel.

What is meant by flavour ? Is it same as taste ?

Ageusia -absence of the sense of taste Hypogeusia -diminished taste sensitivity Dysgeusia -disturbed sense

Vision or Sight sensation

Visible light: 400-700 nm.

The Lacrimal Apparatus: secretes tears during emotions

Tears from the lacrimal apparatus- lacrimal glands→ excretory lacrimal ducts→ lacrimal puncta→ lacrimal canals→ nasolacrimal sac→ nasolacrimal duct.

Wall of the Eyeball

Three layers:

Fibrous tunic- outer layer

Sclera "white" of the eye   (periphery to center)

Cornea-transparent coat

Vascular tunic or uvea- middle layer

Choroid

Ciliary body consists of ciliary processes and ciliary muscle   (periphery to center)

Iris

<u>Retina- inner layer</u>

Optic disc –medial side (blind spot)= no receptors, only nerve

Macula lutea- fovea centralis (midpoint –posterior)

Responses of the Pupil to Light:

Pupil is an opening in the center of the iris.

Contraction of the circular muscles of the iris causes constriction of the pupil.

Contraction of the radial muscles causes dilation of the pupil.

Interior of the Eyeball

Lens- lack blood vessels, consists of a capsule with proteins (crystallins) in layers; transparent.

Lens divides the eyeball into two cavities: anterior and posterior.

Anterior cavity- further divided into two chambers by iris: anterior and posterior chambers. Both are filled with aqueous humor.

Posterior cavity (vitreous chamber)-filled with vitreous body.

Refraction of Light Rays

Refraction is the bending of light rays.

The cornea and lens   refract light rays.

Increase in the curvature of the lens for near vision is called accommodation.

Near point of vision is the minimum distance from the eye that an object can be clearly focused = 25 cm

Refraction Abnormalities and their Correction

Nearsightedness (myopia)- close objects seen clearly. Image is focused in front of the retina. Correction- use of concave lens.

Farsightedness (hyperopia)- distant objects seen clearly. Image is focused behind the retina. Correction- use of convex lens.

Cataracts – older people-cloudy or opaque area or areas in the lens-fibers become denatured, coagulate- impairs vision- surgical removal of the lens- artificial plastic lens inserted

Visual acuity- ability to see objects clearly-20/20 vision-normal vision

Receptors of vision are Rods and Cones

Named after the shapes of their outer segments.

Rod- vision in dim light (black & white)

Cones- three types: red, green and blue (colour)

Outer segment(towards retina)- contains photopigments. Transduction of light energy into receptor potential occurs here.

Inner segment(towards humour)- contains the nucleus, Golgi complex and mitochondria.

Photopigments

Two parts: opsin (four types, three in the cones and one in the rod) and retinal (light absorbing part).

Two types: a)Rhodopsin- photopigment in rods.

b)Cone photopigments- three types- colour pigments

Absorption of light by a photopigment → structural changes.

Bleaching and Regeneration of Photopigment

1. Isomerization: In darkness, retinal has a bent shape called *cis*-retinal. Absorption of photon causes straightening of the retinal (*trans*-retinal).

2. Bleaching: *trans*-retinal separates from opsin.

3. Retinal isomerase: *trans*-retinal→ *cis*-retinal.

4. Regeneration: *cis*-retinal binds opsin

Light and Dark Adaptations

Light adaptation: enter from Dark → light. Faster.

Dark adaptation: enter from Light →dark. Slow.

Cones regenerate rapidly whereas rhodopsin regenerates more slowly.

Light rays- rhodopsin begins to decompose - decreases the outer segment membrane conductance of sodium to the interior of the rod

Rod receptor potential is hyperpolarizing not depolarization

Movement of sodium ions - complete electrical circuit –enter outer segments – exit-inner segments of the rod. The inner segment continually pumps sodium from inside the rod to the outside, thereby creating a negative potential on the inside of the entire cell.

Light= sodium entry stopped, but sodium exit open- hyperpolarized

Dark= sodium entry open- depolarized

Exit is always nonstop

Entry is controlled

Color blindness- inherited inability to distinguish between certain colors. <u>X linked recessive</u>. Only males affected, mother is carrier and transmits to son.

   Result from the absence of one of the three types of cones.

   Most common type: red-green color blindness.

Protanopia-red blind, Deuteranopia-green blind, Tritonopia – blue blind

Testing- Spot charts, Ishiara charts   <u>Eg: pilots</u>

Night blindness or Nyctalopia- vitamin A deficiency.

Strabismus /squint / cross-eye- lack of fusion of the eyes in one or more of the visual coordinates: horizontal, vertical, or rotational.

Pupillary Light Reflex- When light is shone into the eyes, the pupils constrict. In darkness, the reflex becomes inhibited- dilation of the pupil.

Intraocular Pressure

The average normal intraocular pressure is about 15 mm Hg, with a range from 12 to 20 mm Hg- Tonometer

"Glaucoma," a Principal Cause of Blindness- intraocular pressure becomes high to 60 to 70 mm Hg – in elderly

Different colours- perception

If all cones are stimulated equally– white light

If no cones are stimulated, an object would be perceived as black

If many red cones stimulated by a wavelength- red light

When the ratio of stimulation is 13:14:86, the color is interpreted as green light

If red/blue/green cone receptors are stimulated in the ratio of 10:86:15- blue light

If all three cones stimulated different ratios- orange, violet, indigo......

Processing of Visual Input

Receptor potential in rods and cones→ graded potentials in bipolar neurons and horizontal cells→ nerve impulses in ganglion cells→ optic nerve→ optic chiasm→ optic tract→ thalamus→ primary visual area of cerebral cortex in occipital lobe.

Nystagmus -The characteristic jerky movement of the eye observed at the start and end of a period of body rotation is called **nystagmus**

Clinically, nystagmus is seen at rest in patients with lesions of the brain stem.

Hearing sensation

Anatomy of the Ear

Three main regions:

External (outer) ear- auricle or pinna, external auditory canal, and tympanic membrane.

Ceruminous glands- wax

Middle ear- auditory ossicles: malleus, incus and stapes.

Auditory (eustachian) tube.

Internal (inner) ear- Semicircular canals - Labyrinth: bony and membranous. Bony labyrinth- perilymph and Membranous labyrinth- endolymph. Oval window and round window- membranous regions. Cochlea is present

The Internal Ear –

Three parts:

1. the semicircular canals,

2. the vestibule (both contain receptors for equilibrium) and

3. the cochlea (contains receptors for hearing).

Semicircular canals: anterior, posterior and lateral.

Ampulla-dilated

Vestibule consists of two sacs: utricle and saccule.

Cochlea

Snail-shaped.

Section through the cochlea shows three channels: cochlear duct, scala vestibuli and scala tympani.

Helicotrema

Vestibular membrane

Basilar membrane

Spiral organ or Organ of Corti- hair cells.

Neurophysiology of Hearing

Audible sound range: 20-20,000 Hz.

Sound waves→ auricle→ external auditory canal→ tympanic membrane→ malleus→ incus→ stapes→ oval window→ perilymph of the scala vestibuli→ vestibular membrane→ endolymph in the cochlear duct→ basilar membrane →hair cells against tectorial membrane → bending of hair cell stereocilia→ receptor potential→ nerve impulse = cochlear nerve. Excess Sound wave → scala tympani→ round window.

Deafness - two types: (1) that caused by impairment of the cochlea / auditory nerve- nerve deafness- permanent (2) caused by impairment of the physical structures of the ear that conduct sound itself to the cochlea-conduction deafness- Audiometer- audiogram

Neurophysiology of Equilibrium

Two types of equilibrium:

Static- maintenance of the body position relative to the force of gravity.

Dynamic- maintenance of body position (mainly head) in response to rotational acceleration and deceleration.

Receptors for equilibrium are hair cells in the utricle, saccule and semicircular canals and are collectively called vestibular apparatus.

Otolithic Organs: Saccule and Utricle:

Macula- small thickened regions within the saccule and utricle.

Sensory structures for static equilibrium.

Also detect linear acceleration and deceleration.

Contain hair cells and supporting cells.

Stereocilia and kinocilium together called hair bundle.

Otolithic membrane rests on the hair cells and contain otoliths.

Tilting of the head forward→ sliding of the otolithic membrane bending the hair bundles→ receptor potential→ vestibular branch of the vestibulocochlear nerve.

Semicircular Ducts

Crista, a small elevation in the ampulla contain hair cells and supporting cells.

Cupula, a mass of gelatinous material covering the crista.

Head turning movement→ semicircular ducts and hair cells move with it→ hair bundles bend→ receptor potential→ nerve impulses→ vestibular branch of the vestibulocochlear nerve.

Equilibrium Pathway

Hair cells of utricle, saccule and semicircular ducts→ Vestibular branch of the vestibulocochlear nerve →brain stem → cerebellum and thalamus→ cerebral cortex. (opposite side)

Motion Sickness

The nausea, blood pressure changes, sweating, pallor, and vomiting - excessive vestibular stimulation.

Space motion sickness – astronauts-early days of space flight - reentry into earth atmosphere

Origins & Influences of Perception

Visual Cliff test – Babies younger then 6 months can sense a difference between shallow and deep. 6 months and older have a lot of experiences to this point so most react to the visual cliff.

All senses are either inborn or develop early on in life not just sight.

Psychological factors can influence how we perceive the world:

1. **Needs** – more likely to perceive something if we want it or desire it.

2. **Beliefs** – what we believe to be real or not can determine whether we perceive something or not.

3. **Emotions** – emotional responses can a great impact on what we perceive or not.

4. **Expectations** – previous experiences often influence the way we perceive our environment.

Parapsychologists are people who study and try to prove or disprove the existence of ESP

There is no credible evidence that says ESP exists beyond the odds of chance or 25% of the time.

Lesson from the Magician – you cannot always trust what you see or what you think you see. Your eyes are not always the best evidence to find out the truth.

Near death experience (NDE)

Experiences reported by individuals who have been close to dying or who have been pronounced clinically dead and then resuscitated

Researchers hypothesize that...

NDE is a changed state of consciousness

Out of body experience [OBE] is a basic component of NDE

History: scientific study began with Moody (Life after Life, 1975)

150 case reports with these common features:

Overwhelming feeling of peace and well-being, free from pain

Floating or drifting through darkness

Awareness of a golden light

Encountering/Communicating with a 'presence'

Rapid Succession of visual images of one's past

Experiencing another world, meeting past acquaintances

The impression of being located outside one's physical body (OBE)

***Measuring NDE* is done by Greyson's Three Point Scale (1983)**

Lange, Greyson, Houran (2004) evaluated Greyson's scale using the Rasch model

Results:

There is a hierarchy of NDE experiences

OBE is one of the characteristic, basic experiences of NDE

Hierarchy is invariant across gender, current age, age of NDE, latency between NDE and report

Conclusion: Yes, there is a 'core' NDE. Basic structure and semantics are preserved regardless of intensity of NDE and demographics

OBE:

One's visuo-spacial perspective and one's self are experience to have departed from their habitual position within one's body

Disembodiment

Extracoporeal egocentric perspective

Autoscopy

What causes it?

OBEs are components of near death experiences

A fundamental characteristic of NDE according to Lange et al's analysis

Examples of OBE

Suddenly it was as if he saw himself in the bed in front of him. He felt as if he were at the other end of the room,... (Blanke and Arzy, 2005)

Autoscopic Phenomenon

Autoscopy is a visual illusion of your own body.

Three types of autoscopic phenomena:

Autoscopic hallucination: Seeing your double but viewpoint is still from your own body

Heautoscopy: Seeing your double but not sure where you're located

OBE: Seeing your double, but the viewpoint is from your double. Supine position.

No OBE: spatial unity

Deviant self models due to abnormal brain activation

Brain generates the abnormal self: present in not only the clinical populations but also 10% of healthy population

Hard to study in healthy: spontaneous, short duration and happen only once or twice in a lifetime

Alternate theory: OBE reflect the actual projection of a subtle, nonphysical aspect of one's personality in extrapersonal space

Figure: outside of physical body, direction of visuo-spatial perspective: arrow

Other visual illusions of body parts: phantom limbs, transformation of extremities

Failure to integrate multisensory information from one's own body at the temporo-parietal junction (TPJ)

Disruption of phenomenological and cognitive aspects of self-processing, causing illusory reduplication, illusory self-location, illusory perspective and illusory agency

OBE Patients

Predominantly in patients with epilepsy and migraine (Lippman, 1953)

Devinskey et al. 1989

Nonlesional epilepsy

Epilepsy due to an arteriovenous malformation

Posttraumatic brain damage

Blanke et al. 2004

Dysembryoplastic tumor

Induced by focal electrical stimulation

Research studies reveal that most OBEs are related to focal epilepsy in the right temporal and/or parietal lobe.

Conclusion: Yes, there is a 'core' NDE. Basic structure and semantics are preserved regardless of intensity of NDE and demographics

MRI-Based lesion overlap analysis in OBE Patients (Blanke et al. 2004)

Implication of the TPJ in all patients

OBE can be induced by electrical stimulation of the TPJ (2002)

75% of patients had right hemi-spheric brain Damage

Disturbed Own-body Processing

Association to vestibular sensations

Graviceptive (ortholithic) sensations evoked in regions where higher currents induced OBE (Blanke et al. 2002)

Feelings of elevation and floating

180 degree inversion of one's body and visuo-spacial perspective in extrapersonal space

Proxymal vestibular dysfunction (Grusser and Landis, 1991)

Paroxysmal visual body-part illusion

Supernumerary phantom limbs or illusiory limb tansformations

Integration of proprioceptive, tactile and visual information of one's body fails due to discrepant central representation of the different sensory systems

Both of the above are present to lead to OBE

Otholithic dysfunction: inversion illusion in OBE

Visual body part illusions and illusions of entire body: similar neural structures

OBE: supine position

Autoscopic hallucinations or heautoscopy: sitting or standing, cerebral dysfunction leading to aut. Hal. Or OBE depending on position (Denning and Berrois 1994)

Creation of sensory-central representation of one's own body: brain must integrate and weith the evidence from different sensory sources (visual, tactile, proprioceptive and vestibular information): imposing coherence for diminishing incoherence to avoid uncertainty

Inhibition of discrepant inputs (noise)

Disintegration between vestibular (Personal space) and extrapersonal (visual) sensory info both disintegrations are necessary for OBE and are due to multisensory disintegration and deficient vestibular info processing at the TPJ

Visual Body-part Illusions Accompanying OBE

Induced by electrical stimulation at the right TPJ

Vestibular system is designed to detect the position and motion (or acceleration) of the head in space. It is a sensory system.

Multisensory Disintegration at the TPJ Leads to OBE

Temporo-parietal Junction

Core region of vestibular cortex situated at the TPJ including the posterior insula

Implication of TPJ and cortical areas along the intraparietal sulcus in combining tactile, proprioceptive, and visual information in coordinated reference frame

TPJ-perception of body parts, entire body, biological motion, mental imagery with respect to one's own body (not only visual input but movement, thus proving role in multisensory perception)

TPJ-ego-centric visuo-spatial perspective taking, agency, self-other distinction (self at a third person perspective)

Activation in EBA and TPJ code differentially for embodiment

EEG recording, EP mapping, and distributed linear inverse solution (Arzy et al. 2006)

Own body Transformation task (OBE)

Mirror task (MIR)

Results

Generators of MapMIR (top row) were localized at the left EBA and of MapOBT (bottom row) at the right TPJ and left EBA.

Timing of the Activations

TPJ activation was ~50ms later than EBA activation in OBE Task

EBA linded to visual processing of human bodies and also responds to actual and imagined movements of one's own arm (Astafiev et al. 2004)

Spontaneous OBE vs. OBE near death

Spontaneous OBE vs. OBE near death

Spontaneous OBErs "score higher on measures of somatoform dissociation, body dissatisfaction and self-consciousness" (Murray).

Possible causes of NDEs

REM Intrusion

Still have NDES when taking drugs blocking REM.

Cerebral Anoxia &Shortage of Oxygen

Trying to avoid reality

Effects of NDEs

Increased Concern for Others

Reduced death anxiety

Strengthened belief in afterlife

Increased self worth

Different study found higher divorce rate in those who had a NDE, 65%, vs. those who had a "life changing event,"19% (Christian).

Terms

Out-of-body experience (OBE) - Experience of seeing one's own body and the world from a location that is outside one's physical body (disembodiment). This extracorporeal location and visuo-spatial perspective is generally experienced as inverted by 180 degrees with respect to the subject's actual position.

Disembodiment - Experience that the self is localized outside one's physical body boundaries.

Autoscopic hallucination - Experience of seeing one's body in extracorporeal space (as a double) without disembodiment. The double is seen from the habitual egocentric visuo-spatial perspective.

Heautoscopy - Intermediate form between autoscopic hallucination and OBE; the subject experiences seeing his or her body and the world in an alternating (or simultaneous) fashion from an extracorporeal and his bodily visuo-spatial perspective; often, it is difficult for the subject to decide whether the self is localized in the double or in one's own body.

Sense of agency- The ability to recognize oneself as the agent of a behavior or thought.

Visual body-part illusions - Experience of seeing parts of one's own body (generally a limb) as modified in shape, position, number, or movement with respect to their habitual appearance.

Visuo-spatial perspective - The point of view and the direction from which the subject experiences seeing.

Inversion illusion - The experience of seeing the world from a location and visuo-spatial perspective that is inverted by 180 degrees with respect to the subject's actual position and perspective. There is neither disembodiment nor autoscopy.

Room-tilt illusion - The experience that the world is inverted by 180 degrees with respect to the subject, whose experienced position and visuo-spatial perspective does not change. There is neither disembodiment nor autoscopy.

✓ NDE memories = Self defining memories

✓ Crucial to NDErs' personal identities

✓ Highlights importance for clinicians to facilitate their integration within the self

Evidence for Survival After Death Index

(1)NDEs occur while patients are brain dead.

(2)Out-of-body perception during NDEs has been verified.

(3)People born blind can see during an NDE.

(4)NDEs demonstrate the return of consciousness from death.

(5)The NDE study by Raymond Moody has been replicated.

(6)Experimental evidence suggests that NDEs are real

.(7)NDEs can be considered to be an objective experience.

(8)NDEs have been validated in scientific studies.

(9)Out-of-body experiences (OBEs) have been validated in scientific studies.

(10)Autoscopy during NDEs have been validated in scientific studies

(11)A transcendental "sixth sense" of the human mind has been found.

(12)NDEs support the "holonomic" theory of consciousness.

(13)The expansion of consciousness reported in NDEs supports consciousness theories.

(14)The brain's connection to a greater power has been validated by indisputable scientific facts.

(15)The replication of NDEs using hallucinogenic drugs satisfies the scientific method.

(16)NDEs are different from hallucinations.

(17)The replication of NDEs using a variety of triggers satisfies the scientific method.

(18)Apparitions of the deceased have been induced under scientific controls.

(19)People having NDEs have brought back scientific discoveries.

(20)NDEs have advanced the field of medical science

(21)NDEs have advanced the field of psychology.

(22)NDEs correspond to the "quirky" principles found in quantum physics.

(23)The transcendental nature of human consciousness during NDEs corresponds to principles found in quantum physics.

(24)NDEs have advanced the fields of philosophy and religion.

(25)NDEs have the nature of an archetypal initiatory journey.

(26)People have been clinically dead for several days and report the most profound NDEs.

(27)NDEs have produced visions of the future which later prove to be true.

(28)Groups of dying people can share the same NDE.

(29)Experiencers are convinced the NDE is an afterlife experience.

(30)The NDEs of children are remarkably similar to adult NDEs

(31)Experiencers of NDEs are profoundly changed in ways that cannot occur from hallucinations and dreams.

(32)NDEs cannot be explained merely by brain chemistry alone.

(33)NDEs have been reported by people since the dawn of recorded history.

(34)The skeptical "dying brain" theory of NDEs has serious flaws.

(35)Skeptical arguments against the NDE "survival theory" are not valid.

(36)The burden of proof has shifted to the skeptics of the survival theory.

(37)Other anomalous phenomena supports the survival theory.

(38)NDEs support the existence of reincarnation.

(39)The scientific evidence supporting reincarnation also supports the survival theory.

(40)Xenoglossy supports reincarnation and the survival theory

(41)Past-life regression supports reincarnation and the survival theory.

(42)Contact with "the deceased" has occurred under scientific controls.

(43)After-death communications have been reported by credible people.

(44)Dream research supports the NDE and survival theory.

(45)Deathbed visions support the NDE and survival theory.

(46)Remote viewing supports the NDE and survival theory.

(47)The efficacy of prayer has been demonstrated under scientific controls.

(48)The "Scole Experiments" during the 1990s support the NDE and survival theory.

(49)Astrological concepts have been proven scientifically.

(50)Astrological concepts are found in NDEs.

(51)Electronic voice phenomena (EVP) supports the NDE and survival theory.

(52)Prominent atheists have had NDEs which caused them to believe in the afterlife.

(53)Psychometry supports the NDE and survival theory.

Paranormal activity

Scientists believe in ESP

55 % of natural scientists

34 % of psychologists

60 % of social scientists

77 % of humanities professors

Phasmophobia = fear of ghosts

Spectrophobia = spirits

Demonophobia = demons

Satanophobia = satons

Hadephobia = hell

Wiccaphobia = witchcraft

What does paranormal mean?

Para – outside, beside, on the side of

Normal – what one considers typical

Paranormal is a word used to describe events that occur "outside the range of normal experience or scientific explanation".

What are ghosts?

Ghosts are the manifestation of the soul or the spirit of a person.

Why do they remain?

Traumatic or Violent Death

- automobile accidents

- sudden death

- suicide

- murder

- accidental death

Unfinished Business

- direction to undiscovered items

- comfort loved ones

- desire to seek justice for crime

- watch over body

Unaware they are dead

Bound by grieving loved ones

Forms Apparitions Take

Orbs

Drake House EVP – electronic voice phenomenon

Mist

Shadow People

Waverly Hills

Full-Bodied Apparition

Did you see a face in a hidden object with special format arranged? It is just a coincidence of manufacture. Pareidolia refers to the imagined perception of a pattern or meaning where it does not exist.

Our brain seeks meaning and understanding. When your brain sees this picture and automatically picks out the eyes, nose and mouth of a face, that is pareidolia.

Matrixing is a type of pareidolia – the brain's tendancy to attempt to find things we recognize in what we are seeing and hearing, often assigning human forms or faces

Areas of Paranormal Activity

Cemeteries, Battlefields, Hospitals, Museums and Prisons

So…you think you want to be a paranormal investigator? Here are some things to keep in mind.

- Ghosts were people too. Respect them, respect their space.

- Not all ghosts are bad. Some just want to be noticed, others have unfinished business, some are just bored.

- You always need to protect yourself. Be aware of what you are opening yourself up to. Don't invite what you don't want.

- Ouija boards are not toys. Do NOT play with them.

- Obey rules and laws…if a cemetery closes at 9:00, leave at that time. Do not trespass. Stay out of dangerous and unsafe buildings.

- Plan on not getting any EVPs or having any experiences. Most of the time you won't get anything! This is not a job for the impatient.

- For over five decades, experimenters all over the world have been tape recording 'paranormal voices', voices that are not heard when a tape-recorder is playing but can be heard when the tape is played back. Many of the very short messages claim to be from dear and loved ones have passed on recently. They are responsive, by using the experimenter's name and answer questions. Thousands of researchers around the world have been researching this most fascinating psychic phenomenon. It is quite relevant to the argument since it follows strict scientific procedures and experiments have been duplicated under laboratory conditions by researchers in many different countries. Persistent investigators get critical shock after decided to investigate electronic voice phenomena because by using the proper method of tape recording they are likely to hear voices of loved ones or friends who have died.

How to overcome

Pray every night before going to sleep

Face the fear and dare

Try to stay calm

Read self help books

Use GPS and maps

Make travel trips in morning times

Examples of Paranormal novels

Stephen King novels/movies

Ghost Hunters/Ghost Adventures/Paranormal State/Fact or Faked: Paranormal Files/Paranormal Witness

Paranormal Activity 1,2,3

The Grudge (all)

The Ring (all)

The Others

The Phantom of the Opera

Mothman Prophecies

Paranormal Reality topics

Big Foot

God

Creationism

Aliens

UFO's

Psychics

Monsters.

Faith Healing

Levitation

Ghosts

Conspiracy theories

Channeling

Afterlife

Conclusion:

As the coin has two sides-head and tail when there is god there is evil too. Faith is the pencil of the soul that pictures heavenly things. So, have your faith in god and have a good spirit inside you. Lets make a ceaseless effort not to ridicule, not to bewail, not to scorn human actions, but to UNDERSTAND them. Some things are just absolutely insane....

We can have a chuckle at their expense, but be sure to respect the views and feelings of your peers in the class so as not to make enemies. Discuss but don't Argue!

Paranormal = A subset of pseudoscience

Any phenomenon that in one or more respects exceeds the limits of what is deemed physically possible according to current scientific assumptions. A reliance on explanations for alleged phenomena that are WELL outside the bounds of established science.

Paranormal to Pseudoscience

In late 19th/ Early 20th century:

People started to care

Spiritualists were exposed by magicians.

Today:

CSICOP (1970) - Committee for the Scientific Investigation of Claims of the Paranormal.

3 levels of why belief system is trouble:

1. Philosophical = False beliefs about how the world actually works= DANGEROUS! Eg- Truth=good

2. Practical = The Amish (sorry boys) Eg- Prayer over inoculation

3. Social = Bringing it to the masses = Uncritical acceptance of paranormal belief systems can be extremely damaging Eg- Hitler, World Trade Center

Nevertheless if one accepts faulty evidence, intellectual shoddiness and fraud and twisted logic for little things it becomes EASIER to accept the same type of evidence in support for really bad stuff.

Spiritual World and Physical World

Examples of Spiritual Phenomena

1. ESP – Extra-sensory-perception

2. Auras

3. Telepathy

4. Clairvoyance

5. Psychic healing

6. Mind over matter

7. Mediums and channeling

Lets take a look at some holy scriptures:

Bhagavad Gita 2:17- 20

"No one can bring to an end the spirit which is everlasting.

…the eternal in man cannot die…he does not die when the body dies."

Dhammapada 4:46

He who knows that this body is the foam of a wave, the shadow of a mirage, he breaks the sharp arrows of MARA.

Ecclesiastes 12:7

... and the dust (physical body) returns to the earth as it was, and the spirit returns to God who gave it.

Koran 87:16-19

Behold, you prefer the life of this world;
but the Hereafter is better and more enduring.

Adi Granth, pg. 188

Man wails over the loss of what he calls his; Know,
the self is not perishable.

Basic Questions on spirituality

1. Does the Spiritual World exist?

Answer: "Yes."

2. Then, how does it relate with us?

Lets begin a trip by asking,
"Where am I going?"

Lets start with the final destination in mind.

The final destination of life is death.

Everyone dies !

What happens after I die?

Man's Position in the Two Worlds

1. Microcosm

2. Owner

3. Mediator

Microcosm = Small Cosmos with planning and creating

Owner of Physical World = Physical Self and physical world with five physical senses

Owner of Spiritual World = Spiritual World and spiritual self with five spiritual senses

Mediator = between spiritual and physical world

The Spirit Self needs the physical body to grow.

Figure 1- Relationship Between Physical Self & Spiritual Self

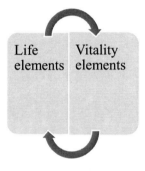

Figure 2- Spiritual Growth Requires a Physical Body

Srimaladevisimhanada Sutra - (TB, pg. 41)

"His body is nourished by food: his spirit is nourished by teaching and experience."

I Corinthians 15:44

It is sown a physical body,
it is raised a spiritual body....

Quran 6:164

Each soul is responsible for its own actions; no soul will bear the burden of another.

Bhagavad Gita 2:22

As a man leaves an old garment and puts on one that is new, the Spirit leaves his mortal body and then puts on one that is new.

Adi Granth, pg 22

"Deal only in that commodity which
shall accompany you after death."

Three Phases of Life

Womb-Liquid - 9 months = Preparation for physical life

Earth-Air $\pm$ 90 yrs = Preparation for the spirit world

Spiritual Love – Eternity = Eternal happiness attending God

Conclusion: We got to live lives of goodness because the spirit world exists (according to our scriptures).

Fundamentals of Spiritism

Existence of god

Existence of spirits and their survival after death

Reincarnation

Multitude of inhabited worlds

Communicability of spirits

Figure 3- Most Basic Elements of the Universe

God, the supreme intelligence and the first cause of all things, created the two universal elements: spirit ("the intelligent principle of the universe") and matter ("intermediary agent, upon which the spirit acts").

The existence of a spiritual life was mentioned by Jesus consistently in the Gospel. If this life exists, spirits live there. **But what are spirits?**

Spirits are the intelligent beings of creation. They constitute the world of the Spirits, which pre-exists and outlives everything. (SB, item 23)

Some critical questions:

What is spirit's innermost nature?

It is not easy to explain spirit in human language. For common man, it is nothing, because it is not something palpable; nevertheless, for us it's something (it's an objective reality as substantial as the body is to you).

Is spirit synonymous with intelligence? Intelligence is one of spirit's essential attributes, but both merge into a common principle; thus, for layman they are one and the same thing.

Is spirit independent of matter, or is it only a property of matter, as colors are properties of light and as sounds a property of air? They are distinct from each other, but the union of spirit and matter is necessary to enable matter to act intelligently.

So are there two general elements in the universe – matter and spirit? Yes, and over everything is God, the creator and author of all. These three elements comprise the principle of all that exists – they are the universal trinity. But to the element of matter must be added the universal fluid, which plays an intermediary role between spirit and matter

According to Spiritism, the soul is a real, distinct being, the cause and not the effect of all human activities. It explains that spirits are nothing more than the souls of people who lived materially on earth. It means that when people are incarnated the spirit is called the soul but when the body dies it is called the spirit.

God never stopped creating spirits thereby peopling several inhabited world in the universe. And Jesus said: "in my Father's house there are many mansions", John 14:2.

All spirits created simple and unenlightened, with an equal aptitude to progress by their individual activity. Each one of us, through reincarnation, acquired the experiences that made us what we are today.

Among the many teachings that Spiritism brings us, there is this triple configuration: spirit, perispirit, and physical body. The perispirit is the intermediary that connects the spirit to matter

Spiritism teaches that the Spirits:

Are not created at the moment of the physical conception;

That all will attain the degree of perfection compatible with human beings by their personal efforts;

Being (all them) children of the same Father, are objects of an equal solicitude;

They are created unceasingly, during all times;

After the death of the physical body they compose the spiritual population of the Earth.

Survival of the Soul

Only the life of the spirit is eternal; the life of the body is transitory and temporary. When the body dies, the soul returns to the eternal life. (SB, item 153)

Even before considering ourselves to be human beings and the offspring of our parents, we are in reality Spirits, God's children.

The existence of spirits has no end.

Spirits can be imagined as a flame, an ethereal spark.

Whenever an intent thought is, that is also where the spirit is.

Each spirit is indivisible.

The spirit can extend its thoughts in all directions.

Figure 4 – Connections

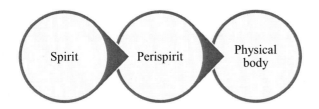

EVIDENCE OF THE EXISTENCE AND THE SURVIVAL OF THE SPIRIT

The evidence of the existence of the Spirit is given by the consciousness that the person possesses of itself (consciousness of its self) and by the manifestation of its will. Spiritism renders it clear and distinct when these beings (the Spirits) prove their identity through countless verifiable indications, referring to individual particularities during their life on Earth.

In current days, the evidence of the survival of the Spirit can be certified:

Through mediumistic communications and psychic phenomena;

Through past life regression;

Through experiences of Transcommunication: spiritist messages by means of television, video, computer, telephone, recorder, radio etc.

Experiences of the Spirits through photographs.

What is the destiny of spirits?

Every human being is an incarnate Spirit on its way towards God.

Life on Earth is always an opportunity to make amends and learn as we travel along the pathway towards goodness. There is free choice in all things and the consequences, either good or bad, are the result of our own decisions. This is the law of action and reaction, of causes and their effects. If we are suffering at this moment it is possible that the cause of this suffering comes from errors in this life or from previous ones.

Therefore, if we commit evil, then sooner or later we will undergo the consequences of that act. Jesus said: "Each according to his works." This explains the reason for so much suffering in the world.

This is why one person progresses more quickly than another, just as do different students in the same class. The better the conduct the quicker we are able to liberate ourselves from suffering, thereby shortening our path towards evolution.

"Do you not know that your body is a temple of the Holy Spirit, who is in you, whom you have received from God? Therefore honor God with your body."

   Paul–I Corinthians, 6:19 &20

"The body is the first loan received by the incarnated Spirit."

   André Luiz – Conduta Espírita

Man is a <u>Spirit,</u> He has a <u>Soul</u> and lives in a <u>Body</u>

We Choose How we Live Spiritually With our Mind

When The Spirit of God operates In us- "it Draws People"

…….to Live Life More Abundantly

Why Should Care Partners Reconnect Spiritually?

In Order to Serve Others in Unconditional –

Love

Joy

Peace

Long-suffering

Gentleness

Goodness

Faith

Meekness and

Temperance

Living By Our <u>SOUL</u> (mind, will, emotions or intellect) Can Negatively Effect People Living With Dementia and Draw People Away From Us As Care Partners

Scientists Suggest that Mankind Was Wired for Love (Optimism Bias)

Prion Proteins send out wrong signals in brain from chaotic rogue thoughts - Draws People Away From Us?

Traditionally the fields of clinical psychology and psychiatry have operated in the Medical or Disease Model. In the Disease Model the health practitioner looks for what is wrong in the patient, or what disease process is present. Once the disease is diagnosed it is corrected by a cognitive or pharmacological intervention. The focus is on the negative aspects of the Mind and Brain.

However recent research has shown that there is a 'optimism bias' wired into our brains. We seem to be 'wired for love, in other words, we are wired to expect good things for ourselves; we are wired for the positive.

It has been shown that this bias has a positive impact on our mental, physical and financial health This discovery is at the core of the recently emerging fields of Positive Psychology and Positive Psychiatry.

In contrast to being wired for love, we have to be conditioned to fear according to Pavlovian principles. In other words even though we are naturally wired for love, we have to learn fear.

There is even a state called 'Learned Helplessness' in which a person has to be forced into- a type of depression. In summary, therefore, the preponderance of evidence is pointing to the fact that we are wired for love (positivity) and we have to learn fear (negativity). This will have huge implications in the health care industry.

75 % to 98% of the illnesses that plague us today are a direct result of our thought life

The average person has over 30,000 thoughts a day.

Through an uncontrolled thought life we create the conditions for illness; we make ourselves sick

Research shows that FEAR, all on its own, triggers more than 1,400 known physical & chemical responses and activates more than 30 different hormones

Toxic thoughts causes the following illnesses: diabetes, cancer, asthma, skin problems and allergies just to name a few.

The association between stress and disease is 85%

80% of cancers are due to lifestyles and are not genetic

98% of diseases are lifestyle choices and therefore (thinking)

Toxic thinking literally 'wears down' the brain and the rest of the body

Research Study: How Bitterness Affects our Health and Mind

If we hold on to resentment, it can grow into bitterness. Bitterness affects our health, our mind, our personality, our relationship with family, loved ones and our relationship with God.

According to studies, Doctors have found that there is a huge relationship between forgiveness and health. The fact is after being hurt, angry, suffering loss, real or false guilt, or envy, the blocked love flow profoundly affects the way your body functions, thus your health. This can cause alteration in the pattern of chemicals and electricity in your body. It also disrupts the harmony of the brain waves, making you less able to think clearly and to make good decisions.

1. Bitterness affects our health & Mind.

Bitterness is poison to our body. Bitterness, hatred, and unforgiveness can result in ulcers, high blood pressure, and other diseases. It is estimated that almost about 90 percent of our sicknesses are anger, fear, resentment and bitterness related. Bitterness affects the body such as: high blood pressure; sleeplessness; lost of appetite and tiredness. Bitterness takes away joy, peace and happiness.

2. Bitterness affects our thought and feeling.

Most depression has its roots from bitterness, resentment, anger and unforgiveness. Bitterness causes anxiety, feeling of insecurity and restlessness.

3. Bitterness affects our behavior .

Such as sudden outbursts of anger; alcohol, drug, or tobacco abuse; social withdrawal and relationship problems. In other words bitterness alienates us from other people and that attitude can also scare people from getting close to us. And as a result bitterness can detour us from our very best to the extend that life cannot be fully celebrated and enjoyed.

Research has stated - HOW WE THINK AFFECTS HEALTH

Thinking affects all the Body Systems. There is mounting scientific evidence demonstrating the intimate relationship between the Brain, the rest of the Nervous System, the Endocrine System and the Immune System shown by the emergence of the sciences of psychoneuroendocrinology and psychoneuroimmunology. These two fields of medical study and practice are basically shedding light on the how the relationships between thinking, stress, the Brain, hormones and the Body's immune defenses affect psychological and physical wellbeing.

Because Mind controls Matter, therefore, thinking is the pre-eminent influence on health. It has been shown from various sources that 75% to 98% of illnesses are a direct result of our thought life. The association between stress and disease is a colossal 85% (Dr Brian Luke Seaward). The International Agency for Research on Cancer and the World Health Organization has concluded that 80% of cancers are due to lifestyles and are not genetic, and they say this is a conservative number According to Dr Bruce Lipton (The Biology of Belief, 2008), gene disorders like Huntington's chorea, beta thalassemia, cystic fibrosis, to name just a few, affect less than 2% of the population. This means that the vast majority of the worlds population come into this world with genes that should enable them to live a happy and healthy life. He says a staggering 98% of diseases are lifestyle choices and therefore, thinking.

Interestingly Herbert Benson MD, the president of Harvard Medical School's Mind-Body Institute, toxic thoughts lead to stress, which affects our body's natural healing capacities. Toxic thinking literally 'wears down' the brain and the rest of the body.

According to Dr H.F. Nijhout (Metaphors and the Role of Genes and Development, 1990) genes control biology and not the other way around. According to W.C Willett (balancing lifestyle and genomics research for disease prevention Science (296) p 695-698, 2002) only 5% of cancer and cardiovascular patients can attribute their disease to hereditary factors.

According to the American Institute of Stress it has been estimated that 75 – 90% of all visits to primary care physicians are for stress related problems.

Care Partner-Self Care

Self-Care Must Include Being

Physically Healthy

Mentally Healthy

Emotionally Healthy

Financially Healthy

Spiritually Healthy

Ideas For Getting The Help You Need

Talk to family, friends, neighbors, co-workers

Setup medical appointment, psychiatrist

Talk to counselor/case management/social services

Support Group/social group/community connections

Clergy, spiritual needs

Legal Services, financial counseling

In-home care

Stress reduction, meditation, healthy eating, relaxation

Client Centered Care Begins in Care Partner's Home First

Allowing The Presence of God to Operate In Us

Is The Spirit of God In Our Home?

Home Life Affects the Care that a medical doctor Provides to Clients

- Arguments

- Division

- Strife

- Bitterness

- Unforgiveness

- Lack of compassion

- Peace

- Forgiveness

- Understanding

- Love

- Joy

- Long-suffering

- Gentleness

- Goodness

- Faith/Trust

- Temperance

- Communication

- Compassion

- Patience

- Meekness

Unity In The Home…Flows Outwardly

Serving in the Spirit of God - For People We meet Anywhere

At Work: What Spirit Do We Operate In?

Our Attitude Continues in the Work Place

Serving In Your On Strength

Where is God's Love in Us?

Walking in the "Fruit of the Spirit" of <u>Love </u>Changes Everything

To Walk in The Fruit of The Spirit of <u>LOVE</u>

<u>Love is…</u>

Love is patient.

Love is kind.

It does not envy.

It does not boast.

It is not proud.

It does not dishonor others.

It is not self-seeking.

It is not easily angered.

It keeps no record of wrong.

Love does not delight in evil.

But rejoices with the truth.

It always protects.

Always trusts.

Always hopes.

Always perseveres.

Love never fails

Serving in the "Spirit of God's Love" Takes a Team Work Approach

God's Presence In the Work Place

Finding ways to provide support for co-workers needs:

Physically (Body)

Socially (Soul)

Spiritually(Spirit)

God's Spirit Operating In Us

We Are Triune Being

Body

Soul

Spirit

Just as God (Trinity)

God the Father

God the Son

God the Holy Spirit

Providing a Person-Centered-Care Approach

Reconnecting: Spirit, Soul & Body

In the Way We Know Best

We All Need Godly Wisdom

No One Individual Has all the Answers

BUT THE GOD THAT CREATED US ALL DOES HAVE THE ANSWER

Every Individual Needs Spiritual Wisdom

Every Group Needs Spiritual Wisdom

Love is…

Love is patient. Love is kind. Love does not envy. Love does not boast. Love is not proud. Love does not dishonor others. Love is not self-seeking. Love is not easily angered. Love keeps no record of wrong. Love does not delight in evil. Love rejoices with the truth of God's Word. Love always protects. Love always trust God. Love always hopes. Love always perseveres.

Self care must be:

Physically Healthy, Mentally Healthy, Emotionally   Healthy, Financially Healthy,
Spiritually Healthy

Spiritual Love in operation: In self, In family, In traveling to work, in the

community, and anywhere we travel, in us with our co-workers individually,

as a team approach and to care enough to put in place a spiritual/religious

care plan /program that meets the needs of the PERSON LIVING WITH

DEMENTIA on a daily basis.

Action Plan – exercise to make spiritually fit

<u>God's Kind of Love Never Fails</u>

What corrections could you make in your personal life that would change how people positively think of you?

What changes could you make to positively effect your family life?

What changes could you make while traveling to work and in the community?

What changes could you make in yourself that could help make a better work environment for you and your staff or co-workers?

What could you do to help improve the quality of life for your person living with dementia?

How could you make changes to bring unity and hope to the families of the person living with dementia?

Spiritual/Religious Questions Answered for/by a Person Living With Dementia: Person Centered Care

Questions that may be included in an assessment of spiritual/religious needs

Who or what provides the person with strength and hope?

Does the person use prayer in their life?

How does the person describe their spirituality?

How does the person describe their philosophy of life?

What type of spiritual/religious support does the person desire?

What is the name of the person's clergy, minister, chaplin, pastor, rabbi etc…?

What does suffering mean to the person?

What does dying mean to the person?

What are the person's spiritual goals?

Is there a role of church, synagogue, temple etc…in the person's life?

How does faith help the person cope with illness?

How does the person keep going day after day?

What helps the person get through the healthcare experience?

How has illness affected (mental, physical, emotion, addiction etc…) in the person and his/her family?

Is religion/faith and important part of their life?

How has faith influenced their past and present?

Are they apart of a spiritual or faith community?

Are there any spiritual needs they would like to explore or discuss?

The Spiritual/Religious Needs of People Living with Dementia Using a "Team Approach"

Include in Assessment :

person living with dementia

spouse

family

friends

closely connected neighbor

co-worker

supervisor

church member

pastor, clergy, priest, minister, teacher, counselor, rabbi, etc…

anyone close to person with dementia

Supporting a Spiritual Lifestyle

By Allowing God's Presence to Abide

Nurturing the person living with dementia and their family with joy, hope, faith, love and service.

Serving by Activating the "Spirit of a Servant" In You

Committed Servants in the work place

Unity &Love for co-workers and not demanding your on way

Serving the Clients with love and compassion

Nurturing the families with joy, hope, faith, love and service

Handouts /Resources Provided to student learning

1. Supporting a Spiritual Lifestyle: PowerPoint Presentation

2. Spirituality and Mental Health

3. The Influence of religiosity and Health

4. The role of spirituality in health care

5. Spirituality and Ethics in Business

Divination

The art or science of deducing the future or the unknown through the observation and interpretation of some facet of nature or human life, ordinarily of an unpredictable and trivial nature.

A preternatural or supernatural or occult means of gaining knowledge (of the past, present, or future) and also guidance normally.

Creative speculation: a means of gaining knowledge based on extrapolating from known facts by means of the imagination.

According to Walter Liefield (1976:146-147) mentions six different methods:

1. Chresmology (Telling the future by seers), (i.e. Samuel prophesying that Saul would be king)

2. Oneiromancy (the interpretation of dreams), astrology, horoscopes, signs of the Zodiac

3. Necromancy (consulting the dead),

4. Haruspicy (the study of animal entrails),

5. Augury (the analysis of movements of animals, especially birds),

6. Mechanical means (the observation of water, fire, casting of dice, rods, or arrows). Gideon's fleece and the Urim and the Thummin would be classified here. America, Ouija boards, Phil: spirit of the glass.

Mesopotamian methods of divination

Extispicy ~ divination using animal entrails

Lecanomancy ~ divination by dripping oil in basin of water

Oneiromancy ~ divination through dream interpretation

Why do people practice ancestor veneration?

For the following reasons

1. Respect

2. Blessing/prosperity

3. Tradition (Confucian in China/Korea)

Power Concepts

Adapted from Love, 2000, 24.

Power persons-imams, shamans, pastors, priests

Power Objects-charms, amulets, talismans, etc.

Power places—Mecca, Springfield(?), saints' tombs, Kaaba stone, temples, Catholic churches, natural habitats such as mountains, caves, (remember Otis's theory), terebinth (oak) trees. (Boniface and Thor's tree).

Power times-Muhammad's birthday, the Hajj, Hindu pilgrimages, Catholic town fiestas (Lady of Penafrancia).

Power rituals-prayers, incantations using the Koran, the Bible or other religious books.

In order to minister effectively in animistic situations, we got to know spirit world vocabulary and operation sufficiently to be able to use specific terminology to exactly communicate into their worldview.

Types of cult institutions

    1. individualistic

    2. shamanic

    3. communal

    4. ecclesiastical

        1. Olympian

        2. monotheistic

Individualistic cult institutions

not performed by specialists

each person enters into his or her own relationship with supernatural entities

requires no intermediaries

examples:

        vision quests

        hunting magic

        "luck"

        "children's cult

Shamanic cult institutions

involve part-time practitioners

involves simplest expression of religious division of labor

examples:

shamans proper

diviners

medicine men

palm readers

astrologers

Universal Human Needs and "Cultural Institutions"

obtaining food

hunter

gatherer

farmer

passing on culture

parent

teacher

securing shelter

explorer

builder

procuring goods

producer

trader

merchant

Now a days in the modern world, divination appears to be less widespread than in the past. Fewer forms are in common use than in the past. Many forms are highly simplified.

Types of divination:

1) Inductive = Based on the observation of exterior signs which can indicate facts through a symbolic link, a sympathetic connection, or through divine intervention or miracle.

2) Intuitive = Based on the interior apprehension, through a natural innate ability or divine aid, of facts.

Inductive - By Signs, Omens, and Prodigies

By Examining Animal Entrails (Haruspicy)

Through Physical Features (Physiognomy) – palm reading

Through the Stars (Astrology)

Intuitive - Through Oracles or Prophets

By Staring at a Point (Scrying)

What is a Shaman?

saman – an Evenk (Tungus) word meaning one who is excited, moved, raised" in the strict sense, a Siberian or Mongolian spiritual practitioner

Anthropological Understanding of Shamanism

not a single, monolithic religion

a cross-cultural form of spiritual practice, typically serving the needs of the shaman's society a cultural universal

Core Functions of Shamanism

maintain and restore health within the group

maintain and restore balance between the group and the rest of the universe

provide humans with a sense of control over the world

Because.......

the natural and cultural worlds exist prior to our birth, we must develop relationships with these preexisting worlds, most of these relationships are learned from others

Shamans Address the Human Needs to

- secure food
- heal disease
- cope with death
- comprehend the universe

Securing Food

locating game

ensuring continuity of animals

maintaining harmony with the animal world

Healing Disease

diagnosing causes

determining treatments

combating spirits

retrieving souls

Coping with Death

explaining causes of death

guiding the soul into the afterlife

freeing the soul from attachment to the living

Comprehending the Universe

explaining the cosmos

cosmology

mythology

exploring the cosmos

divination

Shamanic Training

often acquired from an established shaman

primarily via language and observation

usually takes place in consensual reality

posits – and provides for experience – of extraordinary realities → essentially traditional

The Shamanic Journey

leave ordinary reality to travel to extraordinary realities like drumming, dancing, plants, chanting and return with knowledge

Shamanic States of Consciousness

are culturally defined

are repeatedly encountered

expand the cultural world view to encompass extraordinary realities

affirmation cultural tradition

The Shaman's Answers are obtained in multiple realities

realities defined by culture

reflect learned models

culturally conservative

are obtained by transcending realities

suspend cultural realities

break down learned models

culturally innovative

Represents a methodology to acquire answers that will maintain tradition - conservative effect

Entails a possibility for generating answers that go beyond tradition - innovative effect

Shamans Teach Us that there are multiple realities, that the mythic is real, to serve others, to maintain harmony with the universe and that the quest has both personal and social dimensions.

So You wanna be a Shaman

- be prepared to "die"

- be willing to serve others

- be open to experiences that most people do not want to face

Neurophysiology of Shamanism

Hmong Shamanism is a tradition which is very old and passed down from generations to generations.

Shamans are a key figure in the Hmong culture and religion. Only a few are chosen to be Shamans in each of the Hmong families. Being a Shaman means a big deal to those who still practice the old ways of the Hmong culture.

There are some tools that a shaman uses to prepare and perform at certain rituals and ceremonies. Shamans aren't made and neither are they born. It is believed that during a persons life they will be chosen by the spirits and will become very sick. It is believed that you will dream about riding horse and going over mountains, and then your family will call forth a shaman. To perform the first ritual to see if the spirits have really chosen you to become a shaman.

One of the rituals that a shaman would perform on a person who has been ill is called, "Calling the spirit". It is believed that when a persons spirit leaves their body the will become very sick, and the shaman will come and perform a ritual to go look for the spirit and call it back into the sick persons body.

Shaman also known as "Medicine Man" "Witch Doctor" or "Sorcerer"

Induces ecstatic trance states to communicate with the spirits

This allows shamans to heal, communicate with the animals, control natural elements (fire, rain), and other magical feats

Ecstatic Trance States:

1. The physiological response

Mind becomes focused

Nervous system detaches itself from external sensory input

Reflex inertia & involuntary nervous responses

2. The emotional response

    Continuum of emotion

    Awe, love, sadness...

3. The intuitive perception

    Consciousness is expanded

Depth of Trance

Light trance

    Pulse and breathing rate slows

    Reluctance to move, speak, think or act

    Visual illusions may occur

Medium trance

    Illusions of touch, taste and smell

    May experience cataplexy

Deep trance

    Able to open eyes and not affect trance

    Positive and negative hallucinations

    Sensations of lightness/floating

Able to control visions and dreams

Neurophysiology of the Shaman

General theories

Activation of the sympathetic and parasympathetic systems

Very deep rest induces the "letting go" experience

Shamanic induction procedures

Extensive motor behavior

Auditory driving

Fasting and nutritional restrictions

Sensory deprivation & stimulation

Hallucinogens

Extensive motor behavior

Dancing causing hypoglycemia and release of endogenous opiates

Auditory Driving

Drumming, singing, or chanting - Synchrony in alpha and theta waves in electroencephalogram [EEG]

Fasting and nutritional restrictions

Fasting induces hypoglycemic state

Food & water deprivation

Effects the pituitary and adrenal glands

Stimulates the hypothalamus & hippocampal-septal systems

Nutritional deficient

changes in the CNS

Influence serotonin synthesis

Sensory deprivation & stimulation

Increase cortical synchronization

Greater sensitivity to parasympathetic stimulation

Slowing of the alpha band along

Emergence of delta waves

Loss of serotonin inhibition

Hallucinogens

Use of psychoactive plant substances

Hallucinations

Visions

Seizure induced ASCs

Parasympathetic dominance

Healing Practices of Shamanism

Oldest healing tradition in the world

Soul Retrieval

Extraction of Spiritual Intrusions

Physical Ailments

Consciousness and Healing

Drumming, Music

Dance

Community

Psychedelic Drugs

Long-term psychosis

Unpredictable effects while high

Low abuse potential (no "reward circuitry" dopamine   component,   animals won't self-administer)

"Classic" Hallucinogens
LSD, psilocybin, 2-cx, mescaline

Very few human studies, have to rely on animal "head twitch" models

5-HT2A (sub-type of serotonin receptor) main site of action; correlation between binding and hallucinogenic properties = necessary & sufficient [7].

Synthetic Psychedelics

Potency at 5-HT$_2$ receptors:
LSD ~= DOI > DOB >> DOM >
5-MeO-DMT > DMT

Can roughly rank hallucinogenic properties

But also have additional action on serotonin system

5-MeO-DIPT (Foxy)

Blocks SERT (serotonin removal from synapse, like cocaine, SSRIs)

Rats find it "like LSD, but not exactly"

- Same for 2C-T-7

- May be less intense: also activates $5-HT_{1A}$, which inhibits $5-HT_{2A}$

Potential long-term effects

- Toxic to petri-dish serotonin system (Nakagawa, Sogawa)

- Giving it to adolescent rats → worse cognitive function as adults → serotonin system damage? (Compton)

Neural biology of Healing:

Music/Drums

- GSR

- muscle tension

- heart rate/blood pressure

- mood/attitude

- decrease EMG responses

- reduces pain

- audioanalgesic mechanisms

Dance

- Opioid Mechanism

- triggered by the A-delta mechanosensitive afferent nerve fibers

110

- reduction of pain

- enhanced tolerance of stress

- stimulate immune system functioning

Community

- also involves Opioids

- emotionally charged cultural symbols

- placebo elicitation of opioids

LSD

- Sensory

- Behavioral

- Emotional

- Cognitive

Schools and programs exist all around the world where people learn how to become a shaman. Used in mainstream culture as a way to help "lost souls"

Defining ordinary waking states of consciousness versus altered states is culturally and linguistically constrained

Previous Western views depicting shamanic practices as fraudulent and deceptive have been overturned by findings that neurochemical changes do occur as a result of these practices.

Human Nervous system divisions

1. Central NS = brain + Spinal cord

2. Peripheral NS = Nerves =

a) Somatic NS = voluntary

b) Autonomic NS = involuntary

c) Enteric NS = involuntary

Divisions of Autonomic Nervous System [ANS]

ANS =

1. Sympathetic nervous system (fight / flight)............SNS

2. Parasympathetic N S (feed + breed).....................PSNS

ANS regulates unconscious activities in body

Complementary to each other

Sometimes opposing each, but work as a team to achieve a common goal

Origin of SNS =

In thorasic vertebra

In spinal cord

In lateral grey column

Intermediolateral nucleus

Leave spinal cord through anterior root

Form sympathetic chain of ganglia

Flow of signals is bidirectional depending on situation

Origin of PSNS

4 cranial nerves =

Occulomotor nerve number – 3

Facial nerve – 7

Glossopharyngial – 9

Vagus – 10

3 spinal nerves = nerve cell bodies in lateral grey horn of spinal cord

Sacrum segments S2, S3 and S4

Sympathetic Effects

Fight, Fright or flight response

Release of Neurotransmitters (NT)-

Norepinephrine (NT) from postganglionic fibers

Epinephrine (NT) from adrenal medulla

Mass activation prepares for intense activity

Heart rate (HR) increases

Bronchioles dilate

Blood [glucose] increases

GI motility decreases

Contraction of sphincters

Relaxation of

Detrusor muscle

Ciliary muscle

Mydriasis

Parasympathetic Effects

Normally not activated as a whole

Stimulation of **separate** parasympathetic nerves.

Release Acetylcholine (Ach) as NT

Relaxing effects-

Decreases HR.

Dilates visceral blood vessels.

Increases digestive activity.

Bronchonstriction

GI motility increases

Relaxation of sphincters

Contraction of

Detrusor muscle = bladder

Ciliary muscle = pupil size

Miosis

List of normal neurohormones

1. Enkephalins

2. Gamma-amino butyric acid

3. Glutamate

4. Vasopressin

5. Adreno corticotropic hormone

6. Epinephrine

7. Histamine

8. Endorphins

9. Angiotensin II

10. Neurotensin

Functions of the Hippocampus - normal

Hippocampus is the elongated portion of the cerebral cortex that folds inward to form the ventral surface of much of the inside of the lateral ventricle.

Stimulation of different areas in the hippocampus can cause almost any of the different behavioral patterns such as pleasure, rage, passivity, or excess sex drive.

It has a complex role because of its connections

Learning ---lesion cause antegrade amnesia

Hippocampus originated as part of the olfactory cortex

Hippocampus presumably became a critical decision-making neuronal mechanism.

Hippocampus transmits some signal or signals that seem to make the mind rehearse over and over the new information until permanent storage takes place

Necessary for consolidation.

Effects of Stimulating the Amygdala

1. Increases or decreases in arterial pressure

2. Increases or decreases in heart rate

3. Increases or decreases in gastrointestinal motility and secretion,

4. Defecation or micturition

5. Pupillary dilation or, rarely, constriction,

6. Piloerection,

7. Secretion of various anterior pituitary hormones

8. Tonic movements, such as raising the head or bending the body

9. Circling movements

10. Occasionally clonic, rhythmical movements

11. Different types of movements associated with olfaction and eating, such as licking, chewing, and swallowing.

12. Pattern of rage, escape, punishment, severe pain, and fear.

13. Stimulation of other amygdaloid nuclei can give reactions of reward and pleasure.

14. Sexual activities that include erection, copulatory movements, ejaculation, ovulation, uterine activity, and premature labor

Emotions

1. Cognition----awareness of sensation

2. Affect------feeling itself

3. Conation-----urge to take action

4. Physical changes-----Hypertension [HTN], tachycardia and sweating

Centre is cingulate gyrus--------- natural response

Defense response------hypothalamic area

Conditional response

Control of emotional response:

Influenced by social and cultural factors

Mediated by neural and hormonal system

Peripheral system: ------- via ANS depending on type of emotion

Central control:----- emotional expression experience and the sensory information from environment passes through thalamus to hypothalamus.

Animism

Animism encompasses all of life and is a religion focused on spiritual power.

Levels of animistic involvement vary from one society to another.

Know your culture's worldview and that of your host culture and know them well.

Get a deep understanding of animism in your context.

Know your holy scriptures well, especially as it relates to God's response to animistic practices.

Know the four point paradigm for Pentecostal ministry in an animistic context.

Animism is:

Holistic—not separating the sacred and the secular.

Spiritual—all of life is interpreted through a spiritual lens or worldview.

Amoral—the spirits can be either good or bad. For humans, sin is seen as social rather than theological.

Religion of power—gaining it and maintaining it is the focus of animism.

Socially oriented—this is why it is so strong in group oriented societies.

Pervasive and attractive

Breeds nominalism

Virile and Adaptable

The Eight Tenets of Animism

Animism is holistic

-Does not separate the sacred and the secular

-Line between the natural and supernatural worlds is very thin/non-existent.

-We can and should categorize the occupants of the middle zone, noting who they are and what they do, but we need to understand that at the popular these distinctions are often not clearly made

-Some animistic societies have a cyclical view of life/reincarnation.

Animism is spiritual

-the realm of the spirits is very active in the affairs of men

-spirits can impact the realm of men and men can impact the realm of the spirits through charms, incantations, sacrifices, pilgrimages, etc.—All of which is done to manipulate the spirits to do the will of the person or at least keep the spirits from causing harm.

Animism is Amoral

-Since most spirit beings can either be good or bad, reflecting that there is no well defined concept of right and wrong as it relates to supernatural powers.

-The theological implications of this need to be thought through. (Ill. Little concept of eternal judgment)

-However, there is a strong concept of getting revenge (Ill. Lady in Borongan)

Animism is a religion of power

-the drive to attain spiritual power outweighs other considerations such as ethics or morals

-A religion that has no power has no appeal to the animist—The tendencies of Western theology to present the Christian faith in a rational manner hold little, if any, appeal, to the animist. What does this say about a powerless Christianity? (Ill. Charles Kraft and the old man. The lady cab driver in Thailand.

Animism is Socially Oriented

-Particularly strong in cultures that favor a group orientation.

-Many rites and rituals involve festivals, group sacrifices and other community events.

-Rites of passage become important and can be either individual or community events.

-In group oriented societies smooth interpersonal relationships among those of the same group including, the unborn and the ancestors (aka living dead)

-the rest of the supernatural world-goal is to live in harmony with both the human and the spirit world.-Sin is seen as social, an offense against the family, clan or community, in both the natural and supernatural realms, more than an affront to a Supreme Being.

Animism is pervasive and attractive.

-It is totally anthropocentric

-It is concerned with daily needs.

Christianity (especially Western) asks "Do you want to go to heaven when you die?"

-The animists asks "How can I make sure that the rice crop is abundant and that my children remain healthy?"

-The Bible addresses both issues!

- Humans have an innate desire to control to their world.

Animism Tends to Breed Nominalism

-It is utilitarian. People perform animistic rights when they need something. Otherwise, they prefer to be left alone.

-It does not ultimately call for anyone's permanent allegiance to anything or anyone outside of one's social group.

Animism is Virile and Adaptable

-While the core principles of animism discussed here are the same all over the world throughout history, how animism is practiced changes with the various cultures and over time.

In Vietnam "...spirit mediums give sense to contemporary upheavals of social and historical change. These transformations in ritual practice and spirit representations are likely to bring up to date this long tradition and attract new worshipers." (Chauvet, 86 in Andreas and Lauser, 2011)

-It can also adapt to any formal religious environment

Animism is dangerous! sometimes

Supernatural Causation:

At the worldview level, animistic practitioners believe that the occupants of the supernatural realm are active in human affairs as a matter of course in daily life.

As long as spiritual power is acquired and maintained, animists seldom concern themselves with where the power comes from. They will give their allegiance to whatever spirit or spiritual practitioner can provide what they want. When that spirit, god or practitioner can no longer give them what they want, they simply go looking for another who can.

Spiritual Practitioners and Their Roles

Spiritual Practitioners stand between mankind and the spirit world, contacting the spirits on behalf of people and trans channeling messages and spiritual power from the spirit world to the people.

They serve as mediators or negotiators between the two realms.

Kinds of Spiritual Practitioners

Healers

Shamans

Sorcerers

Prophets, Messiah figures in some forms of animism (Lola of Guinobatan)

Fortunetellers—the masters of divination

Assemblies of God pastors and missionaries! (Barangay secretary in Villasis, Pangasinan)

One missionary to Nigeria saw so many miracles that unbelievers considered him a shaman.—Charles Kraft

Spiritual Practitioners are in Contact With the Spirits

Esoteric Experiences

Witchdoctors receive their calling through some sort of esoteric experience such as a vision quest, dreams or visions. They believe that the spirits empower them to heal.

Practices: Maintaining the Power

Once power is gained, it must be maintained.

Periodic rites and rituals—which will differ from place to place.

Strictly observing related taboos—which, again, differ from place to place.—
Breaking the taboos means a loss of the power and may result in the spirit's getting
revenge and cursing the practitioner.

Can People Be Controlled by an Evil Spirit?

A logical conclusion of the Waray belief in the existence of evil spirits is that these
evil spirits can possess humans. When asked if people could be controlled by an
evil spirit, 81.1% of the general population responded affirmatively and 85.4%
percent of the A/G agreed with them. The difference between the two groups here
was not statistically significant.

Holy Spirit Possession

1. Person is always aware of their surroundings and can remember what they did
   when under the Spirit's power.

2. The Holy Spirit desires a relationship with us.

3. Speaking in tongues is not like a incantation. The power is in the source, not
   the words

4. The power of the Holy Spirit is a clean power.

5. The Holy Spirit always moves to bless people.

6. The Holy Spirit works with our spirit.

Demon Possession

1. Person will not be aware of what they do when possessed.

2. The demon does not desire a relationship with the person they possess. The spirits and the humans involved only seek to use the other. (It's simply a partnership of convenience.)

3. In incantations, the power is in the words themselves.

4. The power of the demons is to deceive, destroy and enslave.

5. Demonic power is never intended to bless people in the long run.

6. The demon dominates the person, pushing their spirit and personality aside.

Community Rituals

One of the tenets of animism is that it is social.

Pilgrimages such as the Muslim Hajj, Hindu pilgrimages, Jewish males three times a year to Jerusalem-Passover, Pentecost, and the Day of Atonement

Ramadan/What does the Bible say about fasting?

Holy Communion instituted by Jesus Himself

Buddhist Festivals/Chinese New Year/

Catholic Town Fiestas

Religious processions—in Catholicism they are done in honor of the patron saint—prayer for rain, healing, protection, etc.

Native American rain dances

Are all community rituals unbiblical/biblical?

Rituals

Religious Rituals are those thought to be sacred or associated with the fundamental operations of the universe. Rituals are effective, hence there is always an explanation for failure, therefore the effectiveness of ritual is not questioned. Rituals must be done perfectly in order to be effective. Rituals are not meant to be understood. Just used for effect. This is where we need diligence to communicate the meaning of Christianity, because, sensing it is religious, the people will not go looking for meaning. They only want to follow whatever ritual they see with it.

To change the ritual is to destroy its effectiveness.

Symbolism is important in rituals. Got to understand what the symbols mean

Communion is symbolic of Christ's crucifixion.

Other Christian Rites and Rituals:

1. Circumcision

2. Passover (Remember)

New Testament

Footwashing

Church membership

Ordination

Anointing with oil

Child dedication

Classifying Religious Rituals

According to Hiebert, two classifications of religious rituals.

Cyclic or Calendrical

Hajj

Ramadan

Kumbmela festival (every 12 years) in India and Hindus

Some Buddhist festivals—Month of the Hungry of Ghosts, birthday of the Buddha

Planting and harvesting rituals as below

Crisis or critical rites

Precipitated by unforeseen events such as plagues, droughts, wars and other disasters. Unlike calendrical rites, these often benefit only a small group or individual. The ceremonies are frequently performed by diviners, medical men or other religious leaders, who claim to have a personal contact with the supernatural.

Values

Some rites, such as the Chinese New Year and Jewish circumcision, connect people to their ethnicity—It's part of their identity. In many cases, religion and ethnicity are tied together. Eg: Malay/Muslim, Thai/Buddhist

Connect people to their past—again, part of their identity.

(Passover)

Connects people to their faith—Hajj

Communion might be considered here, but note that these are trans-local or transethnic. This is one area where communion and Passover must be separated

Can people remain in their ethnic groups and still be faithful Christians?

Other Animistic Issues

Impersonal Forces

Qi

Chi is a primal substance that animates the universe in Taoism, a mysterious force introduced to us by ancient Chinese myths and legends that have also told us about the Tai Chi and about Tao.

Chi is the force that sets the world and everything in it into motion. Chi is also the force that sustains all things once they are created.

Feng Shui

In Chinese thought a system of laws considered to govern spatial arrangement and orientation in relation to the flow of energy (qi), and whose favorable or unfavorable effects are taken into account when siting and designing buildings.

The Dao

In Chinese philosophy the absolute principle underlying the universe, combining within itself the principles of yin and yang and signifying the way, or code of behavior, that is in harmony with the natural order. The interpretation of Tao in the Tao-te-Ching developed into the philosophical religion of Taoism.

Mana

Among Melanesian and Polynesian peoples, a supernatural force or power that may be ascribed to persons, spirits, or inanimate objects. Mana may be either good or evil, beneficial or dangerous. The term was first used in the 19th century in the West during debates concerning the origin of religion.

Kismet or fate

The word Kismet is of foreign origin and is used in Turkish, Urdu, Hindi and Arabic. In Hindi it would be pronounced more like kismat, and it means "fate" or "destiny". The meaning is exactly the same in English. So instead of saying, "it is fate", you could say "it is kismet".

Karma

The law of retributive justice is found in varying definitions in Hinduism, Buddhism and Jainism.

These above mentioned forces are intrinsically neither good or evil. They can be used for both. Just as scientists know how to control empirical forces to achieve their goals, the magician and astrologer control supernatural forces of this world by means of chants, charms and rituals to carry out their purposes.

Totems

Derived from the term "ototeman" in the Ojibwe language, meaning "brother-sister kin," **Totemism** is a characteristic of religious belief centered upon the veneration of sacred objects called totems. A **totem** is any animal, plant or any object, natural or supernatural, that connects deeply symbolic meaning for a person or social group. In some cases, totems may imbue particular person with a feeling of power and energy. In many scenarios, a variety of totems can serve to demarcate particular groups or clans subsumed within larger tribes. Frequently, totems are considered as representative of desirable individual qualities, or the natural power from which a given social group has descended. Hence, totems aid in explaining the mythical origin of the clan while reinforcing clan identity and solidarity, and as such, killing, eating, and even touching a totem is often considered taboo.

Background

No word as 'religion' can be found in the languages of the ancient Near East. Similarly, there is no dichotomy between sacred and secular, or even between natural and supernatural. Only appropriate dichotomy is between the spiritual and physical, though even that would be a less meaningful distinction to them than it is to us. In conclusion, a distinction exists between the earthly realm and the heavenly one, but the events in the two were often intertwined or parallel. Its quite baffling to discuss with ancients the concept of divine intervention, because accordingly worldview deity was too integrated into the cosmos to intervene in it. Always mostly, deity is on the inside, not the outside. Every experience was considered religious experience, all law as spiritual in nature, all duties were duties to the gods, all events had deity as their cause. All Life was religion and religion could not be considered as compartmentalized within life.

Inside the Bible, there are multiple passages which have connotations refering to animistic practices & beliefs, reflecting on how well the biblical authors addressed the issues of their day.

In thinking analytically this, we can explicitly comprehend that biblical theology is never separated from the realities of daily life. That would do well if make sure that our preaching, teaching and writing reflect this view as well.

Mythology

Some rites and festivals maybe connected to cultural mythic stories

Meaning of myth

The anthropological meaning of myth is different from the popular meaning of the word, which is that myths are stories that are not true or made up by people.

Most cultures have their own myths about the world and, more specifically, their ethnic group, was created. (i.e. kami gods of Japan?)

Whether the myths are true is not the point. The power of the myth is in the symbolic stories that they tell that answer people's questions about life. (i.e. some believe this about Adam, Eve and the garden of Eden).

Ritual dramas, especially through dance and music, retell the stories over and over again to new generations.

The Purpose of Function of Taboos

According to Hiebert taboos are the prohibition of certain acts on pain of supernatural punishment. Taboos have at least two functions

Ceremonial cleanliness or purity

-Old Testament laws for food, touching dead bodies, dealing with human excrement or feces and many other things.

-Sanitation was important, but it was not likely the main reason for these laws. I would need to research this more closely, but they probably had more to do with the pagan religious practices of the nations around them than with sanitary issues (i.e. cooking a baby goat in its mother's milk).

<u>Handling supernatural power</u>

Gives better understanding and coherence with supernatural

Supernatural power, like fire or high voltage, is potentially dangerous if not handled properly. With proper rituals and in the hands of those who know the procedures, it can benefit the user, but in the hands of the ignorant, it can be disastrous. The latter thus avoid supernaturally charged objects and places with feelings of awe and fear.

Amulets and Talismans

Amulets can be worn, buried under houses, tattooed on the skin and used in a host of other ways. Generally speaking, they are used for protection against evil spirits or to control spiritual power in other ways. (i.e. St. Christopher's medal or baby's necks.

Talismans, which may be worn in much the same way as an amulet, are generally used to bring good luck, business success, etc. Eg Sacred Heart of Jesus or Mary, rosaries, etc., here in the Philippines.

Others are regular corporate events involving the community and are normally overseen by a religious professional like a priest, etc. Examples of these would be:

The Chinese New Year

Philippine town fiestas

The Jewish festivals of Passover, Pentecost and Tabernacles. Kumbh Mela every 12 years at 4 different sites on the Ganges River

The Muslim *Hajj*

References:

Arzy, S., Thut, G., Mohr, C., Michel, C.M., Blanke, O., (2006). Neural Basis of Embodiment: Distinct Contributions of Temporoparietal Junction and Extrastriate Body Area. The Journal of Neuroscience, 26(31):8074–8081..

Blanke, O., Arzy, S., (2005). The Out-of-Body Experience: Disturbed Self-Processing at the Temporo-Parietal Junction. THE NEUROSCIENTIST, ISSN 1073-8584.

Blanke, O., Mohr, C., (2005). Out-of-body experience, heautoscopy, and autoscopic hallucination of neurological origin Implications for neurocognitive mechanisms of corporeal awareness and self consciousness. Brain Research Reviews 50, 184– 199.

Brumblay, RJ. (2003). Hyperdimensional Perspectives in Out-of-Body and Near-Death Experiences. Journal of near-death studies, 21(4), 201-221.

Cancer Statistics and Views of Causes Science News Vol.115, No 2 (Jan.13 1979, p.23.

Eliade, Mircea. Shamanism. Princeton: Princeton University   Press, 1964.

http://channel.nationalgeographic.com/the-numbers-game/videos/psychic-powers-or-prank/

http://fusionanomaly.net/secretlifeoftrance.html

http://www.dailymotion.com/video/x4lkvym

http://www.massgeneral.org/bhi/research/

http://www.radiov.com/main/beam/features/secretoftrance/

http://www.shamanic-healing.de/englisch/heilerschule.htm

https://people.howstuffworks.com/taoism-and-chi.htm accessed October 19, 2017

John H. Walton, Ancient Near Eastern Thought and the Old Testament: Introducing the Conceptual World of the Hebrew Bible, (Grand Rapids: Baker Academic, 2006), 87.

Langdon, Jean and Gerhard Baer, ed. Portals of Power.   Albuquerque: University of New Mexico Press, 1992.

Lange, R., Greyson, B., Houran J., (2004). A Rasch scaling validation of a 'core' near-death experience. British Journal of Psychology, 95, 161–177.

Lommel, P.V., Wees, R.V., Meyers, V., Elfferich I., (2001). Near-death experience in survivors of cardiac arrest: a prospective study in the Netherlands.THE LANCET, 358, 2039-2045

Murphy, T. (2001). The Structure and Function of Near-Death Experiences: An Algorithmic Reincarnation Hypothesis. Journal of near-death studies, 20(2), 101-118.

Paul Hiebert, "The Flaw of the Excluded Middle," in Missiology: An International Review, vol. 10.1, 35-47, (January 1982), 42.

St. Charles, Il: Church Smart Resources, 1996: 15-38.

Theology in Context: A Case Study in the Philippines (Baguio City, Philippines: APTS Press, 2013.

Van Deusen, Kira. Singing Story, Healing Drum. London: McGill-Queens University Press, 2004.

Winkelman, Michael. Shamanism: The Neural Ecology of   Consciousness and Healing. Westport: Bergin and Garvey,   2000.

www.lenzyhouse.org

www.urbandictionary.com, accessed October 19, 2017.